BUSH PILOT!

DORCEY WINGO

Also By Dorcey Wingo

WIND LOGGERS

THE RISE AND FALL OF CAPTAIN METHANE:
AUTOBIOGRAPHY OF A MAVERICK

CAPTAIN METHANE AND HIS
FINELY FEATHERED FRIENDS

BUSH PILOT!
The Final Adventures of Captain Methane

Text copyright 2021 © Dorcey Wingo
Illustrations copyright © Chris Rohrmoser
Author Photo by Dennis Freeman

Lyrics on page 43 by The Box Tops,
Tony Bennett, and The Animals (in that order)

Published by Smoking Hole Productions
ISBN-13: 978-1-945824-55-5
First edition • December 2021

To Lourdes

CONTENTS

FOREWORD

Although Dorcey and I have never met eyeball to eyeball or put our feet under the same table, I've been fortunate enough to experience his insightful creative energy as part of my life for many years now.

Dorcey the writer and Chris his faithful illustrator sidekick. Batman and Robin. That's how it's been for the past fifteen or so years. Collaborating from a distance, we've embellished many a strange-but-true story for each issue of *Vertical* magazine, the pulse of the helicopter industry.

Fueling Dorcey's acute imagination are piloting, courage, action, humor and slapstick. Humor, above all, is never far from the surface. His flying tales strap you into the right seat of many a helicopter adventure. Better yet, they often plunk you right into the pilot's seat and behind the controls.

Working as an illustrator to transform Dorcey's words into dynamic artwork has always been a personal delight. Without fail and even after all this time, I still eagerly look forward to his latest story. It reminds me of being a kid waiting for the next and newest *Fantastic Four* comic book to hit the newsstand.

We now have a fresh collection of helicopter tales to savor right here in Dorcey's fourth remarkable book, *Bush Pilot!*

Buckle up tight and enjoy these new adventures!

—Chris Rorhmoser

INTRODUCTION

Coming back from an unpopular war in Southeast Asia, about the only thing I had going for me was an addiction to helicopters that I hoped would morph into meaningful employment someday. I had become obsessed with flying machines, mainly helicopters— *especially* Hueys, by then.

A brief, stormy marriage behind me and heartache lighting the path ahead, I faced the reality of the situation: few flying jobs, regardless of how many employment applications I filled out. Restaurant work filled the void for three years. I flipped burgers *before* the Army *and* afterward.

Then, with an uptick in government contracts requiring helicopters, veterans like me found work and began training for new skills, something other than hurling lead downrange, exposing ourselves to death on a daily basis. Ditch the machine guns and hook me up to a bucket, *please!*

Firefighting got me pretty excited about going to work. The civilian version of the Huey was a great machine for delivering big buckets of water and moving firefighters into tight spots—and back out when they're done. This was desirable work for a rookie pilot, inspiring me to embrace mountain flying and hot-and-high challenges with resolve—not to shirk or be a whiner.

The key to enjoying helicopter utility work is to accept the inherent risks of working down low "in the Deadman's Curve," as early aeronautical regulators penned it. This happens to be where our most meaningful work is done, so helicopter pilots who *fear* the curve either need to rethink their fears or accept safer work with fewer risks. Flying a desk comes to mind.

So (before I met and married a wonderful lady) I opted for the bachelor life and those "faraway places with strange sounding names," when given a choice. This attitude took me to South America, most of Mexico, Canada, Alaska and most of the central and western states. I was reminded of Frank Sinatra's version of *"Nice Work if You Can Get It,"* almost every day.

Saving lives or homes from scorching flames; rescuing war refugees or injured climbers; flying famous people to fabulous places; dangling flying saucers at nocturnal mega-rock concerts; moving equipment around on skyscrapers; squeezing rappelers into hover-holes; setting fresh telephone poles in burned-out fire zones; teaching logs to fly; or taking your children for their first flight under those noisy, exciting rotors? Helicopter work was the perfect job for me.

Growing up an amateur cartoonist, I found Al Capp, Walt Kelly, Virgil Partch, Charles Schulz, Gahan Wilson, Gilbert Shelton—and most of the artists in *Mad* magazine—to be more relevant than my required courses in high school. At the time, Khrushchev and Castro were planning to nuke us! They weren't very funny. I desired a little humor instead.

Once in the Army, humor and artwork took a long hiatus with a few exceptions. A TAC Officer had me paint an ornate flying Cobra helicopter on the barrack's first floor, something I'd never attempted but found satisfying, having not screwed it up.

After earning my wings, I was sought out by pilots and mechanics needing custom "Blackjack" logos hand painted on the nose of their Hueys. They had to supply me with "the paint, the brushes and a bottle of Portuguese wine—with cheese, if you please."

Once I was a free man again, I stocked up on colorful pens and sketchpads, making my restaurant employers smile by embellishing boring safety posters and news flyers.

On a road trip to New Mexico with a cat and traveling buddy, Steve Mankle, we documented a memorable trip mile by mile, and all the strange happenings that took place. After our trip was over, I produced a crude cartoon book, *"The Unexplained Undertakings of Chump and Klutz."* I spiced it up with kidnappings, overt drug use, car wrecks, evil spirits, and a deranged hitchhiker.

Following my first civilian flying job, I began taking my sketchpad along, drawing impractical flying machines and caricatures of colorful people I met and/or worked with in the field. It was fun to share cartoons with friends and workmates, but truth be told? After producing over forty pages of esoteric helicopter humor and nonsense, I wasn't satisfied with any of my work.

Then one day, while waiting in one lobby or another, I cracked open a copy of *Flying* magazine. Thumbing through the pages, I came upon an illustration that caught my attention: a pilot resembling a lordly Moses was orchestrating over the controls of a flying machine, making life-or-death decisions as if God, painted on the ceiling of the Sistine Chapel. Perfect!

All *this* to complement a brief story by an avionics technician, troubleshooting radio static in an old twin-engine airplane! I thought to myself, this is *my* kind of cartoonist. I knew I could never match Chris Rohrmoser's talent, but after that article, I began looking for more of his work, envisioning a day that Chris might illustrate a story by a certain roving helicopter gypsy.

When *Vertical* magazine came upon the scene, those of us flying helicopters commercially on the North American continent took note. Suddenly there was a high-quality periodical about our industry that featured outstanding aerial images of new machines, machines at work, and pertinent articles by high time pilots who wrote well enough to earn their own columns. In a stroke of genius, the publishers secured the services of Chris Rohrmoser, adding his touches to the last page in the magazine: a column called *"There I was..."*

Not yet an author in those days, I still knew I could entertain folks with true tales about life under the twirling rotors. I saw an opportunity to share humorous, learning situations and pass along valuable experiences in the quarterly column's prescribed "nine hundred words or less."

So I set to work, a true novice at limiting stories to a certain space—without violating the King's English to the point the magazine wouldn't have anything to do with me. I submitted two or three stories and waited quite a while with zero feedback to encourage me.

And then it happened: checking my email one morning, there was one from *Vertical*. It was a high resolution, full color Chris Rohrmoser rendering of one of my stories! The text that came with the artwork asked for my blessings on the image before they proceeded with publication. There was also money involved. *Yippee!*

Mr. Rohrmoser inadvertently drew one too many main rotor blades on the model helicopter mentioned in the story, so I got busy using a Photoshop program to edit out the extra blade. It became a group endeavor.

I found this exchange to be a shot in the literary arm. By then I had retired from flying and was going through my pilot logbooks, old photographs and many notes, spending hours documenting all that I could remember about many poignant experiences from around the globe.

From this energy came my first book, followed a few years later by my autobiography and then a third book. My second and third books were enhanced by several Rohrmoser images. In *Bush Pilot*, I have embraced the Rohrmoser-Wingo relationship full-on. With the blessings of *Vertical* and Chris Rohrmoser then, here are the remainder of my illustrated stories for your review.

It should be noted that "In a Tight Squeeze" earned a Rohrmoser pictorial, but the story was "not a fit" for the magazine, since the naughty pilot in mention did something he shouldn't have. Also, in "Phthirus Passengers over the Pueblos," our bachelor pilot turned into another kind of bush pilot, having been pickled with cold beer and loud rock music.

So here it is, a chance to live the life of an authentic helicopter "bush pilot" in every sense of the word. It's all true stuff with the exception of one, which shouldn't be hard to pick out. It was my pleasure writing these tales, enabling Chris Rohrmoser and *Vertical* to recreate many memories. I've sequenced them with tales of growing up in Texas and New Mexico, and life in the Army.

BUSH PILOT!

A LITTLE ABOVE AVERAGE

I could always depend on my Mother for an honest appraisal of the given situation, albeit through a Christian/Okie filter. Blanche Beulah could narrow down the important things for me, like why we went to church, spelling rules like "i" before "e" except after "c," or how best to pop a chicken's head off. Blanche was a teacher, but most importantly, she was a survivor.

Blanche was schooled in elementary education, specifically, but she specialized in the fourth-grade level. She presided over thirty energetic ten-year-olds, which required ten hours of work a day, Monday through Friday, with lesson plans and reams of papers to grade on the weekend.

I don't know how Mom did it, but after a day of putting up with fourth-graders, she'd come home and fix dinner for her family of six, and still have the wherewithal to help me with my spelling, geography and arithmetic. She always had the time and energy, when it came to teaching her children.

I remember there was a big deal made about IQs around our house, who knows where it all started. Albert Einstein was still alive when I realized that all men were NOT created equal. A few of us were true geniuses, and some of us were idiots. It's all in the luck of the draw, it seems.

I began to understand the thinking behind hurtful words from childhood antagonists, like *you stupid idiot, blockhead, imbecile, retard, moron, knucklehead* or *pea brain*. These phrases were also

3

thrown around rather casually by big brothers and sisters alike, in practically every other sentence. But not when Mom was around. She wouldn't have any of that, being a Christian.

But being an educator, Mother knew how to measure one's intelligence quotient—through a battery of tests. Mom told us that we would "*never know if or when*" we were taking an IQ test at school. The practice of educators was to disguise these special exams, passing them off as general knowledge quizzes. Their real significance was sequestered, hidden from view.

And for some reason—at an early age—I really needed to know what my danged IQ was, and I figured correctly that Mom already knew the results from the latest tests—so why not come right out and tell me? I pestered my poor Mother about the subject. She politely ignored me.

Then one day after school, Mother and I were returning home down that long, straight concrete sidewalk to Teachers Row. It was a real effort to keep up with her pace and ask my important questions at the same time, but I popped *the IQ query* one last time, and Mom dropped the bomb on me: "Dorcey," she said, "you're a *little* above average."

Not what I was looking for. I knew Mom didn't mean to hurt my feelings. I was hoping for some higher numbers and that wonderful feeling of being blessed with an abundance of brains!

Mom's tone was slightly apologetic. I remember us walking quite a distance without speaking. I recall the energetic drumming of her high heels on cement, setting the tempo for my short legs.

I came to understand over time that one of my two brothers was right up there in terms of smarts. Mom was reluctant to expand on how our respective IQs compared, though. She was hesitant to tell

4

her curious first-grader that *he* was only a little above average—words that could limit his potential, then and forever. Or it could prepare him to do battle with a stacked deck.

It mattered to be smart, I figured. After all, *inferiority* had been pounded into my head by some not-so-brotherly knuckles. "Hickey-knots," he called them. And what about those long, sharp, grass-burrs sister-dear slapped diagonally across my *stupid* face? (I lost that battle.)

The prickly-sharp tines stung for hours after plucking them out, but miraculously, both green eyeballs still worked. I would need them, if I was going be somebody. I was a loud-mouthed, slow-moving weakling compared to my siblings. I would be at their mercy for years to come.

This "a little above average" thing seemed to hang around my neck like a horse-collar after my fateful walk with Blanche. I could forget about being a genius. What was I thinking, anyhow?

A little above average! Which meant to me that I had to study harder and exert myself more than my brainy peers at every turn, or I would languish in mediocrity—an outcome I had been programmed to fear. When Mom's declaration was shortened to "*above average*," it sounded better—but somehow, I longed for more brains than could be shoehorned into my small skull.

So, faced with no better option, I played the hand as it was dealt. I was happy for anyone who was a genius, but I knew that my work was cut out for me if I ever wanted to be somebody. I *did* want to be somebody. A pilot, I dreamed. How smart does a *pilot* have to be, I wondered?

Working part time after high school, I managed to buy a couple of motorcycles. I loved going fast, so to pay for the bikes I did everything from milking cows at a remote family dairy to flipping burgers at night and assembling new bicycles and motorcycles during the day.

Knowing I was only a *little* above average turned out to be a real motivator. Mom couldn't have done me a better service than to downgrade my expectation of entitlement and install something more respectable in its place: *curiosity*, a hard work ethic, and an attitude I could survive with.

My siblings can attest to the fact that I matured to be a fairly good impersonator of my Mother's fourth-grade-teacher's voice and speech patterns. Shifting my vocal chords to *Okie falsetto*, I would go for max-volume: "*Now children, settle down! Today we are going to learn all about Uranus. Stop that giggling, now, and open up your thirty-pound science books to page...*" And so on. I couldn't talk like Mom for long or I'd lose my voice...as if strangled by Blanche!

I got another confirmation of Mom's accurate analysis thirteen years later, when it came time for me to take the Army's Flight Aviation Selection Test, or FAST exam. Just getting to the stage where an individual could take the FAST exam put me in the Army's top five percent mentally and physically, according to a technician who helped navigate my application through the maze.

While one might feel proud about being in the Army's top five percent, the top one percent were the ones who were running things, so no matter what, I was destined to serve under the command of others, risking life and limb, and sworn to do my duty. No more flipping burgers, at least.

There were three of us *applicants* when it came time to get on a military hop in Bangkok and fly way north to Okinawa, Japan, to take the FAST test. The other two men in my unit were both linguists. I had come to know them though our mutual interactions in our unit's Enlisted Men's Club and had played enough hardcore chess with them to realize they were very sharp cookies.

I remember the FAST test was given in a closed chamber with dividers blocking one's view of the others' desktops. I recall there were five phases to the timed exam. There were a lot of multiple-choice questions. There were several questions involving gears, i.e., gear "X" turns clockwise. If gear "Y" were to drop into a given transmission, which way will axle "Z" turn?

Some questions challenged the sincerity of one's military commitments. There were butt-loads of math problems, but no calculators were allowed back then. Wrong answers were sprinkled liberally amid the correct ones. You were either sure of yourself, or you guessed at the answer. All our computations had to be done on the flip side of the respective test page and handed in.

Weeks after returning to Bangkok, our test scores were telegraphed from Japan. My two companions had both scored higher than yours truly. When I read the results, I was reminded of Mom's assessment years earlier. My score, 112, was *a little above average*— but within the acceptable range to fly helicopters for the United States Army. *Yippee!*

As fate would have it, my two smart linguist buddies decided flying helicopters in a war zone was not really what they had in mind, and dropped their mutual applications to flight school.

While Mother was proud of me for earning a pair of wings, she was not looking forward to her two sons going off to war. Brother Jon was six years ahead of me by then, having flown thousands of hours in jets before transitioning to single-engine bombers in the Korean-War era A-1H Skyraider. Jon would swear me in when I got my WO bars, a proud moment for me.

Once flight training was done, we were ordered to Vietnam. Jon and I would both survive, serving under and over service members who exhibited rare courage and unquestionable patriotism. I also served with scores of disgruntled military draftees—some who were *way* smarter—and some who were *dumber* than a stick.

You protected those on your side, and you guarded your six. In the end, fate determined who came home from the war. Your odds were better, though, if you were a little above average.

CHICKEN DINNER!

Blanche Beulah Burch was brought up proud in a God-fearin' Oklahoma family and grew to be a hardworking, educated young lady. She began teaching school right after college. Mom married up with Industrial Arts graduate J.B. Wingo not much later. J.B. knew the hardships of farming: milking cows, slaughtering pigs, raising chickens, and skinning rabbits and squirrels.

My Mom and Dad's relationship was typical of farming families in the post-depression era of Oklahoma. Putting food on the table seldom involved going to a grocery store. A fortunate family had one or two cows to milk and a busy chicken coop to produce eggs and meat.

Their families grew their own food, produced most of their own dairy products, and ate their hand-wrought meals at the dinner table, as a family.

By the time us Wingos moved to Sundown, Texas, there were four of us kids and my parents were local school teachers. We lived in small "teachers' cottages," but the city made up for a lack of square feet by providing a generous space around back for a garden.

Dad and I hauled two pickup loads of domesticated chicken manure to amend the poor soil in order to grow bushels of beans, bell peppers, cabbage, cantaloupe, corn, lettuce, okra, onions, peas, radishes, squash, tomatoes, and watermelon. This was a spring-to-winter, back-breaking, hand-callousing, family project that cut into swimming at the pool and long bicycle rides.

One morning after breakfast, I overheard my Mother making some kind of a deal over the party-line while speaking with Haskell Davis's mom. The conversation concerned the fate of two dozen plump pullets, penned-up over on the west side of Sundown.

Driving to the west side of Sundown—being the one-horse-town it was—only took a few minutes in our 1956 two-door Plymouth Savoy. In a populace of around one thousand, the Davis residence was not hard to locate. Their chicken coop was prancing with white pullets.

Blanche and Mrs. Davis met up on the way to the chicken coop, and amid some cheery chatter, a few dollars were handed over to seal the deal. Somehow my teen-aged sister Joy and I were promoted inside the screened gate of the coop, followed by Blanche and Mrs. Davis.

My sister and I were supposedly needed to help with the slaughter of this fine, feathered flock, but we had never participated in such a thing. We had, however, witnessed the sledge-hammering of a hog's head and solitary beheadings of chickens, as needed for the table.

Mrs. Davis latched the gate at the top and bottom to make sure there were no escapees. Blanche stood ready to her left. There were no knives in their hands. Mom nodded at Haskell's mom and then hunched over like a football player.

Mrs. Davis did the same. In this posture, we learned, they would have better access to the nervous flocks' slender necks. The women jinked toward my sister and me, compressing the herd of *Gallus domesticus*. The ladies looked like they were about to scrum!

By the time both women had their hands around four startled birds' necks, the whole flock erupted in a loud, feathery explosion. The action was center-stage and close up: my sweet, tender Mother deftly snatched her first two victims. Grasping their necks with elbows bent, she wickedly twirled the birds 'round and 'round—three times, in tight, vertical loops. In doing so, she gained the momentum necessary to snap-whip the birds' heads off, like *spaghetti al dente.*

Mrs. Davis, meanwhile, was doing the same. Once deprived of their heads, the chickens in mention commenced to flapping crazy-like and looping within the enclosure, all-the-while spraying hot, red "ink" all over everybody and everything in sight. It was truly amazing to observe how long a headless "dead" chicken could run amok, imitating a live one.

Such little distractions did not slow down the team of Davis and Wingo—who, splattered in red—appeared to gain interest in the mission at hand. Losing little time, they snatched four more birds, albeit with some difficulty—because the word was clearly *out* that *all* the *chickens* were *going* to *die!* Twirl, twirl, twirl, snap-and-die! (Toss the hideous heads behind you.) Twirl, twirl, twirl, snap-and-die! (Toss the heads behind you.) And so it went.

Twenty more mind-numbing decapitations later, my sister and I were getting *some* education: Mom looked like a murderess during all the twirling, and then suddenly dropped her act as if Alfred Hitchcock had shouted, "Cut!" Joy and I had a new perspective at a tender young age. Putting food on the table took on a graphic meaning, one hot afternoon in north-central Texas.

To make sure my sister and I shared in the whole time-honored process, we got to round-up the warm, bloody bodies, load them into bags and pack them into the Plymouth's trunk. After washing up, we drove the flock to Teachers Row.

While we were getting splattered in chicken ink, my Dad prepared a couple of big wash tubs full of hot water in our back yard. After we arrived, he initiated the grim job of cleaning out the birds' entrails. The bucket of resulting gore got a pack of local dogs all excited, thereby complicating our de-feathering mission. We managed to run them off with a water hose.

Then the four of us sat around the stinky, steaming wash tubs, pulling feathers off the birds. They were floating around morbidly therein, while we plucked away at their fine, slippery feathers for what seemed like forever. By the time we finally packed them into the freezer, we had develop a keen dislike for all-things-*chicken*. Steak for dinner, then? That sounded better.

There was one more depressing clean-up job after that: you wouldn't believe how many feathers covered twenty-four chickens. They had to be bagged and secured in a steel trash can.

After writing this story, I shared it with my brother Jon and sister Joy to get their input. Joy admitted that she was so traumatized by that day's activity, she couldn't recall it. But she did ask me if I remembered the 105 "fryers" Mom had us pluck? There was another big chicken massacre in Longmont, Colorado (prior to us moving to Sundown) in 1951. I didn't remember that bloody day in Colorado, probably for the same reason Joy didn't remember Sundown's.

Jon was also quick to respond, pointing out the Plymouth was a '56 coupe, not a '57 as I recalled. He then offered the gritty details about how Blanche caught those pullets one at a time and then handed them to him. He had to tie up each bird by one foot on the clothes line long enough to slice away its head. He then untied the poor critter and let it flop around on the ground until motion ceased. Then into a hot soaking tub they went.

I have no idea how much money Mom saved by doing this slaughtering and cleaning, but it was a lasting lesson in what has to go down in order for us carnivores to enjoy our chicken dinners.

FLUMMOXED!

And Darned to Heck, no Doubt!

Everything was going smoothly at our Sunday evening Bible study, almost done. There were a dozen or so high school and freshman university attendees, in addition to Brother Morton, who presided over the one-hour event. Truly boring stuff this evening, the early chapters of the Bible, with all the "be-gatting."

Behind me sat a row of fragrant females from around Las Cruces, studying the Good Book while our parents gathered in the main assembly, pondering the church's budget and praying for miracles.

Like most young males in my group, I grew nervous as the last few minutes ticked away, knowing the meeting would end with a prayer, and the prayer had to be delivered by a *male*, handpicked by good ol' Brother Morton. No one but me knew it, but I suffered from *glossophobia*, fear of speaking in public.

Not just speaking in public, but talking to **God** in the presence of such lovely young ladies—the ultimate stage on which to stand and deliver. Enduring Brother Morton's intense gaze at the appointed hour, I knew he would soon stretch out his long, bony arm and point that dangerous index finger of his, instructing some poor sucker like me to start praying to God and maybe get us the hell out of here.

"Brother Wingo," he moaned, as if pained by his choice of a victim.

I knew it. "*Pray to God,*" he says. Easy for him.

How hard could it be, just address the Supreme Being and it'll soon be over with.

Start with the standard opener: "Our heavenly Father," I seemed to be hearing my conscience guiding me. This should be a snap; I tried to relax and took a deep breath. And out came these words:

"Our hoverinly fever…" The tangled intro came blaring out of my sixteen-year-old vocal cords and I could scarcely believe it! *Pretend they didn't hear that and fix it,* my mind raced to buoy me.

"Our featherinly hover," was the next errant volley to shout out. I unfortunately have an excellent memory of this event, trust me. Another deep breath, while hoping for a massive coronary.

"Our hoverinly heaver," a waste of oxygen and more fodder for the cannons around me.

I had to admit that I was blowing it big time. Faint snickering from the well-meaning Christians at hand was understandable at this stage of my disaster. *Draw your last breath and try again.…*

"Our……heavenly……Father." Finally. *Now throw in the standard boiler-plate and head for the door!*

"Thank you for this day and its many blessings." I couldn't think of any blessings offhand, and my day had sorta sucked, actually.

"Guide us as we go through the days ahead." Show me a good place to hide, I secretly prayed.

"In Jesus' name, Amen." This is where the bolt of lightning comes through the ceiling, I feared.

I could hear hushed giggles and muttering as the surge of humanity navigated the narrow exit, into the fresh New Mexican air—and away from people who couldn't talk to God.

LIGHTING ONE OFF

Things to do in the dark of night

Turning fourteen years of age, there were discoveries around every corner in my teenaged life. I had hurdled puberty along with my sexually mature pals at school, bringing with it new tones to our voices and undeniable attractions to the opposite sex.

Eager to embrace such new discoveries, a few of us explorers were influenced by our older siblings—if not our fathers—as to the meaning of being a mature adult male animal. Full sexual maturity cannot be achieved, we believed, until the given young stud has struck a match to his ass and lit off a large fart.

Having no Hollywood movies to guide us back in 1962, we nonetheless heard stories that farts contained flammable gases. No one proved that theory to me while I was in Boy Scouts. But the assumption was, *lighting one off* was the next logical hurdle in Carnal Knowledge.

Pondering the solution to my lack of maturity, I spent days analyzing the steps one would have to go through to verify that one's fart had, in fact, ignited. To start with, I would have to have my large colon adequately pressurized to do the job. I would also need to be near the bathroom: a suitable closed space, where I could lock the door, douse the lights and assume the position.

Having rehearsed the critical steps in my brain, I was mentally prepared when Mother's excellent supper of corned beef and cabbage, mashed potatoes and gravy turned into a volatile vapor and started rumbling its way through my guts, toward my nuts.

Taking the time to disrobe, I minimized the risk of setting fire to my clothing, the curtains, etc. A white towel to lie down upon seemed appropriate, as the cement floor is cold in the average New Mexico November. Taking a large box of Ohio Blue Tip kitchen matches down to floor-level with me, I laid myself out next to the electric heater, glowing ever so faintly to my right.

The very first match burst into operation as ordered. I moved the matchbox clear of the blast area. Holding the cedar stick near my white butt with my right hand, I could feel its heat on my fingers, on my right buttock, and thigh. I closed the distance to my bulging orifice and let fly.

The darkness of the bathroom was instantly bathed in a three-second flood of *natural-gas-**blue***. I could see (and hear) the flaming fart perfectly in my reflection off the enamel bathtub. *Methane burns blue!!* And the flame means no lingering odor, except for the sulfur of the match.

I can be thankful that I did not wait a couple of years in lighting one off, as the hairs around my exhaust pipe (think of them as little candle wicks) were comparatively short in those days.

I found out later that igniting methane/nitrogen gas down yonder is a really bad idea. We're talking about serious burns accompanied by lots of pain and days of regret. Don't try this at home!

THE TEXACO MAN

Dedicated to our First Responders

When VA therapists began treating me for Post-Traumatic Stress Disorder (PTSD), I became familiar with a term frequently used in group therapy: "trigger." That is anything which makes a traumatized person feel anxious, uncomfortable—or worse—in recalling a painful event. The patient frequently experiences feelings of withdrawal and survival guilt.

An example: two good infantry buddies are fighting alongside each other in close combat, and one of them is suddenly badly wounded. Amid the chaos, the wounded warrior dies in his friend's arms. Later in life, a loud report or backfire triggers vivid memories of the terrible experience. The survivor mentally withdraws and/or slips into deep depression. This is a situation all too familiar to a combat veteran.

I have experienced combat, but I have different triggers, frankly. Weeping willow tree-limbs trigger awful memories of savage beatings administered by my Father. Seeing any of my Father's heavy, leather belts lying around? More *triggers*. And—family issues aside—the sight of shattered automotive "safety glass" triggers my first face-to-face with death on the highway.

Leaving the dusty high school parking lot that sunny afternoon in May, the 4-door 1962 Chevy Biscayne I was driving home belonged to my parents. With a fresh New Mexico driver's license in my hip pocket, I loved to get behind the wheel. But there was little time for driving around that day, as my school teacher Mother would soon be locking the door to her 4th grade schoolroom in Old Mesilla, and waiting for her ride home.

Westbound on Highway 28, the late afternoon sun was beginning to be a problem. I tried not to drive off the narrow roadway, pulling the sun-visor down low. I came safely to a halt behind a car that was waiting at the stop sign at the intersection of El Paseo Road. A busy truck by-pass cut through the west side of Las Cruces at this point, taking most of the big rigs around town and west toward Deming at highway speeds.

There was no bonafide traffic signal at this busy intersection in 1965, only a flashing red light for west-bound drivers on Highway 28 (like me) to heed, while the on-rushing trucks were warned of the intersection by a flashing *yellow* light. The big rigs had the right of way, that was no secret. It was a dangerous intersection, at best.

The driver in front of me waited for an opportunity to cross, and when his chance came, his chirped his tires, pulling away quickly. I rolled down my window to cool off and was about to pull forward to the stop sign, but something made me stop.

Sitting across the intersection from me was a Ford station wagon full of kids, waiting to cross the by-pass, eastbound. The driver—the mother of those children, it turned out—seemed impatient.

I sensed an impending disaster, so instead of pulling forward to fill the empty space in front of me, I kept my foot on the brake and hesitated. I sat idling, one car length from the stop sign, and about fifteen feet from a stout powerline pole.

Looking to my left, one on-coming tractor-trailer rig was passing another that looked just like it. Here they came, belching four black contrails of diesel as they rumbled northbound toward the intersection, going 55 mph or better.

My heart almost stops beating just thinking about it. My eyes could hardly believe what they were seeing when the lady in the Ford took off in my direction through the intersection, as if the twin, oncoming battering rams of steel and diesel did not exist.

The two semis were perfectly side-by-side when they slammed on their brakes, and they were side-by-side when they smashed into the station wagon packed with children, hurtling the Ford into a wicked, 180-degree-spin. In the next instant, the station wagon snapped off "my" stop sign and wrapped around the power pole, amid a cacophony of wailing tires and shattering glass.

At that point in time, things moved in slow motion. It was eerily quiet. Looking out over the hood of the Biscayne, it was covered in shattered glass. I looked to my right, and saw some men in Texaco uniforms running toward the wreck from a nearby service station.

One uniformed man in particular began wrenching on a battered passenger door, trying to pry it open. The Texaco Man was intent on extracting the injured, his unbuttoned shirt unveiled an Atlas-like masculinity.

In shock at this point, I realized I had barely missed being *wiped out* by the Ford. I then noticed several cars lined up behind me and came back to the moment at hand. I eased off the brake pedal and pulled forward, crunching on a carpet of broken glass.

There was a splatter of glass on the hood of the Biscayne, projecting countless rainbow colors through the angled sunlight.

I then heard moaning and cries of agony that were coming from the crumpled Ford, and gazed out my passenger-side window. The Texaco Man had reached inside the Ford and pulled out a young, crying toddler, with his powerful hands under the toddler's armpits.

The Texaco Man set the inconsolable child down on the ground facing me and turned quickly back to the grim work at hand.

I should have been *in* this wreck, I thought to myself, and yet I am *okay*, and *they* are badly injured—from what the shouts and twisted metal had to say. The child appeared to notice me briefly, his little hands held out in front of him, reaching for anyone.

As a crimson river began flowing from both of his nostrils, I reeled. Sensing the worst for him and all those in the Ford, I felt an unfamiliar helplessness and numbness take over my teenaged body.

Then I noticed a halt to the traffic on both sides of the smoking intersection. I halted briefly where the stop sign used to be, and continued west on Highway 28, safety glass trailing off the car as I drove on. I was trying to come up with words to explain to my Mother what had just happened, and I only had a few minutes to prepare.

The terrible accident at the truck by-pass was the lead story on page one in the next morning's *Las Cruces Sun News*. With a heavy heart, I read that—among those badly injured—the toddler did not survive the evening.

Any time I see a Texaco station, shattered safety glass, or hear a screaming toddler, it triggers an *emptiness* in me that took me almost sixty years to clinically identify, that awful day at the intersection of life and death, and my "response" to it.

Here's to all the real *First Responders* in life.
I appreciate what you are doing, more than you'll ever know.

RUNNING SCARED

It sure beat riding with J.B.

Once my Mom and Dad moved out of Las Cruces for the solitude of country life near the Rio Grande, life got better for them and worse for me. Suddenly we were seven miles *south* of civilization. Since I didn't drive at age fourteen, keeping contact with my schoolmates, bandmates, and related scholastic activities became a logistics nightmare, five days a week.

Getting a ride to school in the morning was easy enough, since Mom was a fourth-grade teacher in Old Mesilla. After she got out, my Father would drop my sister and me off at Las Cruces high school. But getting back to point "A" was another thing.

Mom liked to head straight home around 4pm, but with marching band rehearsals, Monday night band rehearsals, Explorer Scout activities and hot teenaged girls to hug, I was just getting warmed up for one thing or another at that early hour. So I would often end up with no ride home at night.

There were no cell phones back then to call Daddy to come get me and Daddy wouldn't give a big hairy *shit* that I needed a "*goddamned ride*" and certainly wouldn't go out of his way to come get me. It was *my* problem. Catching a ride with my Father became the least desirable way to get anywhere.

Anytime my sister or I created an *"inconvenience"* for J.B. Wingo, we heard about it through halitosis-laden, brow-beating lectures, all the way home. Being told how worthless I was, time after time, did wonders for our relationship. Rolling the window down, I could hardly wait to get out of the fucking car at the next stop, even if it meant walking home alone in the dark. Again.

I seldom had to hike the entire six-point-something-miles to our one-acre estate on the Mayfield Ranch. I had occasional success sticking out my thumb, but "hitching" at night is danger-fraught. And even if I lucked out and got a ride, the do-gooders would drop me off at Carpenter's Store, along the old highway to El Paso. Our mailbox was planted alongside the road nearby.

From Carpenter's it was up and over the railroad tracks and westward for another mile and a half. The road is paved now, but it was a washboard *bastard* back then. It zig-zagged its way past several farm houses, over a wooden irrigation canal bridge, eventually coming to where J.B. Wingo called home.

Nobody would want to drive me home from Carpenter's Store on that dismal dirt road if they'd experienced it before. The county didn't blade the road very often, so it got severely bumpy with all the farming vehicles and families like us hurrying to one place or another, raising the dust.

Dropping me off at Carpenter's was also made possible by purchasing a Greyhound Bus ticket in Las Cruces. The fare was thirty-six cents, one way. I usually had money for the bus, but not always.

The grumpy old bus drivers didn't like to talk and they didn't like to stop at Carpenter's...especially for a *kid*...once they shifted into high gear. The bus would brake hard to a rude stop and leave me standing in the dark, trying not to breath the ugly gray cloud of toxic fumes.

I would walk slowly starting out, allowing my eyes to become adjusted to the moonless starlight. Only then could I see the span of the dirt road. Barbed-wire fences were strung along either side.

On a dark night in mile-high New Mexico, running the mile and a half home was one of the scariest things I ever had to do. I never had a flashlight with me for that leg of the journey: too much to haul if you're running, and no money for flashlight batteries.

Once I could see the road, I started double-timing. I could run all the way home, but the effort would leave me breathless. Walking was out of the question, if you were as scared as I was. There were the *unknowns* in the dark, and the *knowns*. I had to deal with snarling farm dogs ahead, one about every half mile.

The dogs would always hear me coming, even if I slowed down to sneak past the farmhouse. They would alert everyone and everything for a mile around that *somebody* was sneaking up on them in the dark, someone who deserved to be *bitten* and *driven away*.

The anticipation of being mauled prompted me to arm myself with an abundance of rocks scattered along the shoulder of the road. I threw them in advance of my arrival. Caveman artillery in the dark kept my hopes up.

The last big dog to encounter along the road home was spared any of my hard-rock artillery. He was my Dad's German shepherd-mix, "Alphonso," famous for lying in wait in the blackness until I made it to the front lawn. Then he would come flying…one of the dumbest dogs ever…and knock me down to lick my face and welcome me home.

I got my driver's license not long after this. I rarely got to use the family car, so I relied on my two-speed Pugh moped, a Honda 150 Dream, and a Yamaha Big Bear Scrambler in that order, to get me around. I paid for them working nights and weekends at Neff's Topper Drive-In in town.

I discovered that the secret to navigating the washboard portions of our dreaded dirt road was to hit thirty-five mph, which made the tires strike the tops of the bumps more often than not, producing a smoother "ride," if you could call it that. Beats your rig to pieces, though. Our family car rattled like it had rocks in the dashboard.

Later on, on my motorcycles, I found I could go faster than thirty-five-mph over the bumps, but wheels begin to float on their springs under such conditions, leading to uncontrolled yawing and unplanned excursions into the barbed wire and tumbleweeds. Speed and pain go hand in hand.

Riding motorcycles on the dirt road at night brought a new peril. There were many long-nosed "Bull" bats [Leptonycteris nivalis] thriving along the Rio Grande. They came out in the early evening, hunting mice and bugs.

On occasion I would encounter them sitting right in the middle of the road, their wings folded, in the process of eating something. Along I would come on my bouncing motorbike at thirty-five-mph, trying to stay on top of the bumps.

In the stark light of my single headlight's high beam, I would get three, maybe four seconds to react to the *vampire* in my path, knowing full well they rise up at the last second at that speed.

Making contact with a hot-flopping, felt-winged bat was not all that unusual. Having had a thrashing Bull bat bounce off my chest and land in my lap mere inches from Dick and the Nut Brothers, it was all I could do to *not* crash, until the creepy creature and I parted company.

It was around this time that Alphonso got the ax for raiding a neighbor's chicken coop in broad daylight, poor beast. I never shed a tear for him. Dad saw to his demise. J.B. and I, on the other hand, would eventually learn to accept each other. It took a few years.

J.B. actually gave me a hug when I returned home from Vietnam. The road I ran on so scared is now *civilized*, and leads to the Leyendecker Plant Science Center, where the Robert M. Mayfield ranch and family residence used to be. J.B. sold his little acre and moved to Oklahoma in 1975.

As it turns out, *running scared* was good therapy for a young man, less than two thousand days away from being drafted into military service. There would be many times ahead I would rely on my running-scared courage to get me through one harrowing night or another. Fear can swallow you up if *believe* you're going to die. Experience calmed my fluttering heart and kept me going.

A LONG ROW TO HOE

Finding Work and Heatstroke, Too

Most everyone has heard the expression "a long row to hoe" applied to any number of difficulties, i.e. "Serving thirty days in jail for stealing a steak was *a long row to hoe* for Clayton." Or "Pushing my moped all the way home on two flats was *a long row to hoe*."

Or they could very well be talking about the real McCoy: hoeing crops all day in the hot sun. Having grown up in a house full of Okies, the saying was old hat by the time I reached puberty.

By then us Wingos had moved west from the Texas Caprock and settled in the Rio Grande Valley of southwestern New Mexico. Mom resumed teaching fourth graders and Dad started up an antique furniture repair business. It seemed that everyone had a job but my sister and me.

My parents purchased a one-acre homestead nestled deep in the interior of Robert M. Mayfield's cotton and alfalfa ranch, south of Las Cruces and within gunshot of the Rio Grande. Surrounded by agriculture, it was natural for me to join in gathering heavy bales of hay and observing the braceros as they irrigated crops from the river.

Having seen me work, Mr. Mayfield's son Bobby G. invited me to audition as a cotton-thinner on the Mayfield ranch one hot summer morning. The work day started at 07:00, within a mile of my house. The pay was a dollar an hour.

I tied a red paisley handkerchief around my neck, grabbed my water bottle on a rope, rolled up my lunch sack, stuck a straw hat on my size-seven head, put on my work gloves, and grabbed a standard wooden-handled garden hoe. I had a rat-tailed bastard-mill metal file stuffed into my left-rear blue jean's pocket, for maintaining a keen edge on my hoe.

It was kind of tricky making any speed wearing such a large, non-aerodynamic straw hat while clinging to my sack of goodies and the ungainly hoe, but somehow I managed to ride my bouncing bicycle to a decrepit bus that sat parked alongside the road to Mrs. Lee's house.

The worn-out bus was the braceros' cross-border taxi cab. Twenty brown-skinned laborers of every age and description gave me the eye when I rolled up. They paused as they covered their bare necks and tied thick headbands around their skulls to help keep sweat out of their eyes. Others were methodically sharpening their well-worn hoes.

I heard chuckling among the Latin throng when I reported to the tall, heavy-set *jefe,* "Tony Negro." Befitting his name, Tony was as black as the heart of a solar eclipse. He growled my last name as I shook his huge, calloused hand. Looking me over, I sensed he was unimpressed.

"Vamos a ver." *We shall see,* he said.

As for the chuckling, I was to learn that "*wingo*" is Spanish slang for *garden hoe,* the very implement with which we were about to do battle. The formal Latin term for the implement is "*azada.*" I suspect they knew that, too.

For the uninitiated, cotton ranchers plant their fields mechanically. Their tractor-driven, clock-like seed-planting machinery is geared to guarantee over-planting. Following the first good rain or irrigation, untold millions of seedlings sprout and rapidly form long green parallel rows of striving young cotton plants, *Gossypium malvaceae.*

The braceros call cotton seedlings "*algodon.*" The mature plant they call, "*pisca.*" They also used the term *pisca* as a substitute for "whore," and after a life spent toiling in the fields, who would blame them?

Left undisturbed, the young plants grow so thick they rob each other of sunlight and nutrients, stunting their growth and producing a poor yield of cotton for the rancher. It was our job to single out about half of those seedlings with our razor-sharp hoes, and lay them to waste.

At the *jefe's* signal, we each picked a row to hoe. Starting at the end nearest the bus, we chopped our way west. The driver stayed behind with the water and lunches and a couple of camp dogs.

The rows were very long, but probably under a mile. I would soon discover that rows of cotton varied from *bearable* to *overwhelming.* Maybe it was my amateurishness, or I got the latter.

Skilled workers fought off backaches from stooping and weary arms from chopping, bearing down and making *choppin' cotton* look easier than it was. The rookies among us, however, stood in Black Tony's menacing shadow. He was staring unhappily at every stroke of my hoe. When my aim was off and I killed one plant too many, he growled. Tony loved his little cotton plants.

I was surprised at how resilient the stupid plants were—having to take two or more strokes to cut through the tough stems. I attracted unwanted attention with my rookie-like thrashing. I was doing pretty good, I thought, but clearly, I was not going as fast as the average bracero.

My peers' *wingos* didn't look like my hoe, I observed. Their blades were narrower and worn down over halfway from filing the edges away. My hoe was too wide for the thinning process, it turned out—but no one said so.

Re-sharpening my dull hoe became necessary all too frequently, and I lost ground to the braceros the more I sharpened. Braceros must wear out many *azadas* in their lifetimes, I contemplated. The prospect of wearing out a hoe made me want to find other work!

Black Tony noticed my every mistake, grunting his disapproval anytime I left too many standing, or—worse yet—I over-cut, leaving goofy gaps in the crop. The plants were so tight in places, we had to drop our tools, stoop over and pull out the surplus plants manually.

I seemed to have more than my share of these tangled-root bastards, slowing me down even more. When I pulled out a plant, its two neighbors came along with it, tangled up in the former's root system. I created another big gap in the row. Tony Negro was beginning to smolder.

My back was aching before thirty minutes went by, but there were to be no breaks during the hoeing of a row. The promise was, we could water-up and recover briefly at row's end. I made sure my sweat-stained hat shaded the back of my neck—but my neck was already sunburned.

Watching all the little green stems go by, I began to get dizzy. Knowing I was prone to motion sickness, I tried hard to ignore what was happening. We were not yet half-way down the second row when I began to get nauseated. Tony Negro wiped his big black brow and stepped closer.

My eyes were doing so much selecting and sorting and decision making that it was making me queasy. Spitting like a camel, I began to salivate copiously. Sweat poured out of me in little rivulets. *Great Helios* overhead was doing his best to bake my brains into a hot squash casserole.

How on Earth can these braceros do this horrible work, day in and day out, I wondered? I had only hoed the better part of two rows and I was baked. I was about three-quarters of the way to my first sunstroke, as it turns out. The braceros pretended not to notice, but I know they did.

Shit, I was working among some of the most resilient farm laborers in the Mesilla Valley, and they were showing the white boy how to work. *Chop, chop, chop*, like well-oiled machines they toiled, further and further away from where Tony Negro stood hovering over me and my hoe.

When I puked on Tony Negro's cotton plants, I was careful not to tarnish his dusty cowboy boots with whatever it was my stomach so violently rejected. More chuckles from the distant workers.

"*That's all for me,*" I said to Mr. Negro, as I shouldered my hoe.

Tony Negro watched me turn as I slogged back to my bicycle in the "V" between rows, saying nothing. Hours later, my acidic puke would be absorbed by the *Gossypium malvaceae* that survived my horrible hoe, thanks to a nocturnal flow of muddy Rio Grande water.

Later on, I was thinking things over: working at night as they did, Tony's irrigation hands were spared the wrath of the blistering sun. Long hours wading around in the mud in the dark, amid the scorpions and the occasional snake bite? Compared to hoeing cotton? Sounded like a good deal to me. However, it didn't take much investigating to learn that every last one of Tony's employees had worked their way up by successfully chopping Tony's cotton.

In the fall, the cotton matures and the cotton bolls start opening up. The farmers know the plants require a defoliant to help speed things along. The defoliant is applied by grinning, low-level-flying, well-paid commercial ag pilots, flying shiny fixed-wing aircraft.

In the days that follow, the cotton leaves shrivel and the bolls open wide, exposing miles of fluffy white product to giant harvester machines' spinning mechanical fingers.

Spray pilots. Now, there's a job I bet I could handle. As long as they let me toss my cookies every now and then, I'd be fine.

THINGS I LEARNED IN BASIC

The Distance from Private to Drill Sergeant is Ninety-three Million Miles

My 1966 draft notice led to an enlistment in the US Army. The government was more than happy to jet me to Fort Leonard Wood, Missouri for basic training. I was assigned to Company "C," better known as *"Charging Charlie Company"* of the Army's Fifth Battalion, Third Basic Combat Training Brigade. In a whirlwind of high-pressured activity, enlistees and draftees alike were herded into buses and trucked off to lose their hair.

No time was wasted on trainees when it came to our initial GI haircut. Four pissed-off-looking barbers each grabbed a soldier's head with one hand and scrubbed off his hair with loud, overheated metal shears—emulating the *English* with which Australians shear sheep. The faster the barbers worked, the better. Our hair fell into four hairy multi-colored piles, and suddenly we were off to *immunization.*

I was greatly relieved to get our "shots" over and done with. Rumors were rampant from the men one cycle ahead of us. They warned us about the immunization *guns* we would be subjected to. "Don't tense up and don't move, or the gun's stream will slice your arm open!"

They were right about the guns. When the nurses pulled the trigger, there was a shrill sound as vaccine was forced into muscle.

34

Some of the guys next in line were scared stiff and more than one passed out while standing, hitting the floor with a smack.

True to form, some trainees moved when the guns were triggered and its recipients were subsequently cut. Everyone got a Band-Aid, many more were bleeding though them. The guns also raised sizeable knots, painful to the touch. Once our arms were immunized, it was time for our buttocks. At least the Army didn't use their guns on our butts.

We were funneled into two lines like nervous cattle. The room was gymnasium-sized and brightly lit. Two beefy army nurses in white clinic garb wielded large hypodermic needles at the end of the lines. Trainees wound slowly around the room and stopped between the two masochists. A few passed out during this phase and were soundly ridiculed when they came to.

The nurses quickly injected one vaccine or another in either the left cheek or the right, depending on which line you were in. Trainees who passed out or mouthed off in any way were given double-injections. Pulling our pants up, we were soon trucked off to the *quartermaster.*

Drawing our olive-drab GI clothing at the quartermaster, we ran the gauntlet while stuffing our duffel bags with bulky field jackets; two pair of black leather boots, black leather gloves with green wool liners, loose-fitting green fatigues, two web belts with a black utility buckle and a shiny brass buckle for dress, five sets of tee shirts, a few pair of thermal underwear, a clump of long green winter boot-socks, and five sets of green boxer shorts. The bag weighed a ton by then.

There was also one green dress uniform, a dress uniform hat, a garrison cap, a cold-weather cap, a fatigue cap, and some uncomfortable low-quarter shoes that I couldn't see myself wearing, anytime soon.

With NCOs (Non-Commissioned Officers) screaming in our ears at every opportunity, we hoisted, shouldered or dragged those heavy duffel bags as we were marshalled into one of five WWII-era coal-heated barracks comprising Charlie Company. Our eight-week training cycle began in mid-February at the fort known as "Little Korea" for its frigid winters.

I was assigned to the 5th Platoon and probably because I truly *sounded off* when I was told to sound off, 5th Platoon Sergeant Fisher designated me his Platoon Guide, my first lucky break.

As Platoon Guide, I headed the platoon's formations and passed along our platoon sergeant's orders to the men. I shared a semi-private room with the Assistant Platoon Guide. We also dined separately with the Company Cadre and avoided kitchen duty, aka K.P.

Sergeant Fisher was a short, white, middle-aged man who lived in a small room upstairs, not far from where Assistant Platoon Guide Owen Lloyd and I were quartered. Fisher was a glum fellow whom I couldn't picture in an infantry role. But he must have served in the infantry at some point in order to be training new guys, most of whom would soon ship off to Vietnam.

In basic training, one of the first things you are taught is how to kill people. There are several ways to go about killing a human being, other than shooting them. We had to learn and practice the variables, from the neck-snapper to the heel stomp—all were approved and taught by Uncle Sam.

The second thing a trainee is taught: *"If it moves, salute it! If it doesn't move, paint it!"*

One couldn't help but notice the pot belly on our Platoon Sergeant. It looked very out of place in Charging Charlie Company. Company C was famous for its high scores in Physical Training at the end-of-cycle evaluation. I don't recall ever seeing Sergeant Fisher double-time.

Our Platoon Sergeant would dutifully march us along for short distances to various training centers, but when it came time for long marches or double-timing, Sergeant Fisher disappeared. A more fit drill instructor would take his place, resuming the cadence. Reappearing fresh in his intimidating DI hat back at the barracks, Sergeant Fisher would morph back into action when our exhausted platoon returned for evening muster.

So, our drill instructor was a little soft in the middle. I was still happy he chose me to be the Platoon Guide and I did my best to keep him happy. But with forty-eight healthy young men broke and bored to tears, problems were to be expected. Right off the bat, a couple of guys in 5th platoon decided to test the unit's *no alcohol* policy on their first pass to the Base Exchange.

The two were apprehended with a couple of six packs and I had to turn them in, much to my distaste. They were good fellows, just trying to have some fun in an unfunny situation. I spoke with them after their ass-chewing by the First Sergeant. They seemed to harbor no hard feelings.

The thing about Basic Training is, a man's time to himself is rare. There were toilets to scrub, and floors to sweep, mop, and wax. There were boots to shine and rifles to clean, which take more effort than a person might think. Footlockers had to be neat and squared away, dirty laundry secured in green bags with a rope drawstring.

We learned to fire our heavy M-14 rifles from several different positions. We could take the weapons apart and reassemble the pieces in two minutes or less. There was a ton of memorizing to do with general orders, chain of command, rules governing guard duty, on and on.

Sergeant Fisher and I seemed to be getting along famously up until about the fifth week of training. I recall a sunny Saturday that we were allowed some time off to work on our gear. It was pleasantly warm that day, a delight to practically everyone weary of Missouri's cold.

Sitting between the barracks on a couple of green-painted park benches, I was spit-shining my boots along with a few other guys when Sergeant Fisher dropped in on us. We worked in silence for a while, enjoying the waxy smell of black Shinola shoe polish and brass cleaner.

Before long, we were chatting easily about life in general, our thoughts about going to Vietnam, aiming for higher education, and so forth. Then the solar system topic came up, right out of the ether.

I was about to learn our Platoon Sergeant slept through fifth-grade science class, the portion that deals with basic solar system distances and dimensions. When I remarked that the sun was ninety-three million miles from Planet Earth, Sergeant Fisher balked and sat up straight.

He glared at me as if I'd just told him a big, fat lie. "*What's that you say, Wingo? Ninety-three* million *miles?*" I thought he was joshing me at first. I would soon learn a couple more things Sergeant Fisher didn't know.

Our conversation under the sun marked a sudden reversal in the good relationship I had with Sergeant Fisher. He would soon conspire to replace me with my Assistant, Owen Lloyd, who must not have shared my astrological assertions. Lloyd was a farmer from Minnesota. Surely, *he* knew better. It was my bad luck that Fisher never heard of the Greek astronomer, *Aristarchus*.

Shortly thereafter it came time to qualify our M-14s at the rifle range. Sergeant Fisher got in my face before we left the compound and warned me that if I didn't score "expert" that day, he was going to sack me. What a sweet guy. He seemed to get himself off by taking soldiers' stripes.

The *second* thing Fisher didn't know was, I had grown up with a rifle of one sort or another in my hands, and I could flat-out shoot the Army's M-14. Scoring "60" hours later at the range, I could have scored even higher. When I picked off my 60th man-silhouette—one at 400 meters, the private scoring for me shouted *"Expert!"* and I celebrated by firing off the rest of my clip.

When qualifying day was over, I was one of six expert riflemen in Charlie Company, one of two from 5th Platoon. Announcing the results at evening muster, Sergeant Fisher applauded with no smile. He was clearly upset to have his grand plan (temporarily) foiled.

If my Assistant Platoon Guide was in on Sergeant Fisher's secret, he didn't let on. That was until I loaned the 4th Platoon our floor buffer hours before a big inspection. Charlie company was short of electric floor buffers, so us platoon guides had to ration their use.

Owen Lloyd felt I had made a mistake and he challenged me. I told him we'd have to do like the old days and use rags to buff the floors by hand until the floor buffer was returned to us. Off he stomped to tell Sergeant Fisher!

Being a squad leader wasn't all that bad. Oh sure, I lost two of my precious stripes as well as my semi-private room, dining with the brass, etc. At least I didn't have to sleep with a traitor in my room or feed the coal-fired furnaces at night. There was always something to be grateful for.

Like Sergeant Leatherwood, for example. Leatherwood was a sharp looking drill instructor who ran 3rd Platoon like a well-oiled machine. Everyone respected him for his fair-dealing and double-timing alongside our formations, shouting cadences while we were gasping for breath.

Near the end of training, I was one of several trainees summoned to the 3rd Platoon by Sgt. Leatherwood. He said he had a few things to say to us in private. He took off his DI hat in front of us for the first time ever and became dead serious. "You men are getting *FUCKED*," he spat. "Basic training used to last weeks longer. It was designed that way to condition you for combat."

"Instead of marching to and from the rifle range, you have been *TRUCKED* for the convenience of the training schedule. They want to ship you off to Viet-fucking-*NAM*, but you men can't *march* more than a few miles and you *give out*. Charlie will *run you down* because your backs, your legs and your feet aren't properly *conditioned*. You can only get that way by *marching*. And you *haven't been!*" With that, he wished us luck, put his fancy hat back on and dismissed us.

Graduation came and went with the standard military parade. It was a relief to everyone. Long-awaited parents and fragrant girlfriends softened the stark atmosphere around Company C. After eight weeks of nothing but men around, female laughter sounded like angels singing.

No one had come to see me graduate, so I returned to the barracks and packed up for a long bus ride to Signal School. I shook hands with a few of the men who lingered, collecting their gear for the next assignment. Private Tune was among them, the shortest man in 5th Platoon.

Tune had an ever-present smirk on his face that I was initially worried about when the platoon first formed. He hardly ever appeared to be unhappy, challenged by the Army, or his lot in life. Barely five feet tall, Tune appeared bereft of masculinity. Sergeant Fisher might have had his reservations about Tune, too, having never showered with the musclebound midget.

The *third* thing Sergeant Fisher didn't know was 5th Platoon's well-kept secret: *"Not* all *men are created equal."* There was not a swinging dick in the 5th Platoon who was as well-endowed as Private Tune. Ergo the permanent shit-eating grin on this young soldier's face.

TURNING YELLOW

Life and Death at the 106th General Hospital

Life in Bangkok improved significantly after I landed the Enlisted Mens Club manager's job. I was no longer a lowly Specialist E-4 in a dreaded rotating-shift at the distant, depressing CommCenter. Suddenly I had three gold stripes on either sleeve, and no more CommCenter duty for me. Once a month, I donned my army uniform and proceeded to the head of the line at pay call. Not bad for a slightly-above-average, nineteen-year-old, high-school-graduate white boy.

Overnight, Colonel Rovigno had made me an acting Sergeant E-5. My orders were still wet and smelly from the unit's Xerox machine. Because I ran the E.M. club, I would no longer be required to wear a uniform *except* during inspections and pay call. Club managers in Bangkok enjoyed "civilian status," based on the dealings we had with booze and slot machine salesmen.

My new supervisor was a pot-bellied, hard-striper Staff Sergeant E-6. He was the manager of the unit's tiny NCO Club on the Admin Building's fifth floor. *And* an alcoholic from all I could see. His boss was the unit's First Sergeant. Turns out, the two of them were old drinkin' buddies.

Having proven to my boss that I could inventory and dispense alcohol accurately (and open the safe) I settled into my new job. There were older guys in the unit who couldn't stand the fact that a *new guy* could be so damned lucky. The *disgruntled* left typed notes on the Club's bulletin board, criticizing my manner of dress, and my maturity. Ha! I let them stew in their own fat.

With several native Thai employees to do all the work around the Club, there was little for me to do except analyze, organize, deputize, and supervise. This I could do while playing chess.

While sipping a coke in the Club one evening in November of 1967, I was in the midst of a complex chess game with an excellent chess player, and we were listening to the sounds coming from the speakers. (Pawn to KR2.) The club's loud, colorful jukebox was blasting out tunes that made me homesick, i.e.,

"Gimme a ticket for an aeroplane,
Ain't got time to take a fast train.
Lonely days are gone, I'm a-goin' home,
Oh, my baby, just-a wrote me a letter!"

(Or)

"I left my heart, in San Francisco," etc.

(Not to mention...)

"We gotta get outta this place,
If it's the last thing we ever do!"

The music reminded me of at least one lost relationship back in the States. Listening to rock-and-roll love ballads over and over made me melancholy. During an 18-month tour, soldiers endure multiple heartaches. A month seems like a year, especially when you're new. (Pawn to KB3.)

It wasn't long before I began to feel strange. For some reason, staring at the plastic chess pieces was making me nauseous. Tilting my "king" over on his side, I apologized to my chess-mate and cut the game short. I went to bed that evening feeling weak and lousy.

The next morning, I shuffled into the john and passed a disturbing quantity of Coca-Cola-colored urine, a very scary moment! Reporting immediately for "Sick Call," they took my temp and drove me to the hospital in downtown Bangkok. A urine sample later, I was assigned a bed.

Before long, an Army doctor appeared at my bedside, probing my abdomen, taking my vitals and peering into both of my eyes. "You have a fever and appear to be in the early stages of jaundice, young man," the physician stated. "That being the case, you may have hepatitis. You'll likely be transferred to Japan for treatment." *Oh shit, my liver is sick,* I thought. *I'm turning yellow!*

I spent the night in Bangkok's military hospital, sleeping mostly. Awake, I felt awful and unable to eat anything. The mere smell of food made me sick. I had to force myself to drink liquids.

Confined to a stretcher, my first military hop toward Okinawa was aboard a C-130 *Hercules* from Bangkok's Don Mueang Airport to Tan Son Nhut Airport in Saigon, South Vietnam. Offloaded from the C-130, I was transferred to a four-engine C-141 *StarLifter* for the long flight to the 106th General Hospital, with a stopover at Clark AFB in the Philippines for fuel.

I was not alone on these flights; stretchers abounded with soldiers suffering from injuries or ailments I probably didn't want to know about. We were stacked two high along the sides of the fuselage and likewise, in long rows going up and down the center. Very few seats on this bird.

Medical types hustled everywhere, doing a respectable job of seeing to their patients during the long flight. Aside from being weak and yellow, my needs were few compared to the wounded who joined us at Tan Son Nhut for the flight to Japan. They had tubes running in and out of them. They awoke in pain, and we heard their suffering, even over the roar of the shrieking jets.

When we landed at Kadena Air Base, Okinawa, all patients were offloaded into the cold December air that smelled of Jet-fuel exhaust. We were loaded into several waiting busses. The busses were preheated and exclusively equipped for litter patients. Once our bus was full, off we went for the heliport, which was over a mile away, down a badly pot-holed asphalt road.

Our bus driver apologized loudly for all the bumps that he couldn't avoid. I became aware of the "Burn Patient" when they loaded him onboard, he moaned with every breath. When we hit the first ass-kicking bump, the bus shook and rattled loudly. The Burn Patient started screaming at the top of his lungs, "*OHHHH GOD, NOOOOO!!!*" and so on, for the remainder of the bus ride.

Burn patients and hepatitis patients were loaded onto flight-idling, olive-green Huey *Iroquois* helicopters in Japanese markings, and flown to the 106th General Hospital—a five-minute flight.

Having aimed for years to get into the pilot's seat, I couldn't believe I was getting my first helicopter ride on a stretcher! Sitting up as far as possible, I did my best to catch the action in the cockpit. The two pilots' hands hovered over a cool myriad of switches, dials and radios.

Now, there's a job I can aim for, I thought. Digging the rhythm of the rotor blades, I was very impressed with the sounds and smells of rotary-winged flight. This short sortie through Japan's busy airspace served to keep me interested in my lofty goal.

All too soon the Huey was back on the ground and once more, Jet fuel exhaust permeated the chilly air as we were rolled toward the patient entrance of the 106th General Hospital. I was very weary after such a long day. I remember being transferred to a real bed, with medical people lined up to stick me with needles, ask a lot of redundant questions. They were very nice about it.

When I woke up from a long sleep, I took in the sight of twenty-four identical occupied hospital beds all along the opposing wall of the "Hepatitis Ward." On my side of the ward, there were twenty-four more beds. My fellow patients were all men—most were straight from Vietnam—and most were infantrymen. I was the only guy from Bangkok. Word got around about me.

The lanky southerner occupying the bed to my left had yet to be introduced. He was lying there, "reading" a *Playboy* magazine. As I was about to learn, staring at glossy photographs of naked young ladies is not the best idea for a guy who's just had a circumcision, with stitches.

"Lanky" was lying there, reading away, when he abruptly shot to a sitting position, shouting "*OWW!! OWW!! OWW!!*" as he snatched a strategically placed aerosol canister his doctor prescribed for killing spontaneous erections. Which it did, after much needless drama.

Like *Lanky*—I discovered—uncircumcised infantrymen found it near impossible to avoid infections during prolonged bush assignments. Jungle rot and too much time between baths was the problem. The solution was the standard operation, removing the foreskin and stitching up the delicate tissue for a week or so. Lanky opted for the knife, as did a few others. It was free.

There were a lot of "southerners" in the Hepatitis Ward, it turned out. As my strength would allow, I joined in their conversations, getting caught up on what Vietnam was like (aside from all the fighting) and places my fellow soldiers might be interested in going to, in and around the fair city of Bangkok. [They didn't want to know where the zoo was, just the best *go-go girls.*]

We talked about the fighting, too. They laid it out there and I listened to their tales of courage under fire, leg-paralyzing fear, hostility for those in authority, and months of prolonged misery.

There was a tall, thin, black dude in the bed to my right who seemed to like my style, and I his. He seemed to be recovering from hepatitis, his energy showed. "Willy" had poise and delivery. He was quite animated and friendly. He was always asking, "*How 'ya gonna act?!*" There were many things to be outraged about in *this mans' army*, so Willy used the expression often.

The biggest plus about the Hepatitis Ward was the incredible food prepared in the hospital's street-level mess hall. Once we were signed off to walk to the chow hall [usually by the 2nd or 3rd week] dinner was well worth waiting for. This was the best chow the Army had to offer, from all the selections of meats, fish, veggies, rolls, breads, cakes and pie prepared for our joyous consumption. Beside the great seasonings, I never saw an unattractive dish served at that facility.

Doctors occasionally called us patients in for counseling, more probing of our livers, and checking our weights again to see how we were doing. I remember weighing a gaunt 130 lbs. when I got there, down from my usual 155 lbs. My hospital gown hung from me like a tent.

It was common for the doctors to challenge us using simple math problems, just to see how quickly we could process a subtrahend from a minuend—"*....and what is the dividend?*"

Hepatitis is famous for slowing down a person's thinking, as it did mine. I remember complaining to the doctor when I couldn't concentrate, *"Why are you doing this, Sir?"* He explained the problem and why he did so. "Doing the math" improved commiserate with our livers' healing. When livers function, the bloodstream clears up and eyeballs lose their yellowness.

Not everyone recovered from hepatitis, I am sorry to report. Our first casualty was bedded straight across the ward from me. They pulled the sheet up and over his poor head, wheeling him out on a gurney through the double swinging doors. It got real quiet in the ward after that.

Nobody seemed to know much about our late comrade, beyond his name. He had been in bad shape since his arrival, and never made the turn to the better, like most of us. Life isn't fair.

An assignment that came with being a patient in the Hepatitis Ward was cutting and folding bandages in our spare time. Boxes upon boxes of carefully folded bandages, destined for patients in the Burn Ward: to the left and down the hall. We reverently referred to them as *crispy critters*.

We were asked to scrub our hands and fill large boxes with carefully folded gauze bandages every day, as staff couldn't keep up with the demand. More likely, they had better things to do. Burn patients had to have their bandages removed and replaced daily. The dreaded *peeling* process was said to be excruciating. The screaming was hard to bear, even two doors away.

This was in early December of 1967, the date of the first successful human heart transplant. The news was televised into our ward and well received. I think we all got a boost from leaping such hurdles in medical science. *Surely* they can get us over our hepatitis and send us on our way?

After around five weeks, I made the turn toward being healthy again. I had gained over twenty pounds, thanks to the excellent chow and limited exercise. Willy was looking like a healthy specimen, too, so we hobnobbed together over to the mess hall, the BX (Base Exchange), and the hospital's impressive library. I spent hours there, taping *Beatles* albums to take home someday.

One fellow hepatitis patient who became a real pest was this guy I'll call "Leroy." Another southerner and from what I could tell, Leroy was dumber than a hubcap. He had a bad habit of saying, "*You know?*" following every statement he made.

After a few weeks of Leroy hanging around my bunk, following Willy and me around, I was pretty much fed up with him and his "*You know?*" routine. I found Willy's interrogative, "*How 'ya gonna act?*" much easier to take from an intelligent gentleman.

Then we started getting passes. It was great to get my energy back and see the sights around Yokohama. We were not supposed to drink alcohol due to our fragile livers, but that didn't stop guys like Leroy from going out and getting plastered and coming back to hover over my bunk late at night, asking really stupid questions that always ended with, "*You know?*"

Early one morning, Leroy came in drunk, again. He started *hanging around*, annoying Willy and me and everyone else who was trying to sleep. Yelling at him and telling him to **shut-the-fuck-up** only encouraged him, as if he never had any real friends in his screwed-up life, except for us.

Two hours later, Leroy was finally snoring in his bed at the east end of our row. I nudged Willy's bunk with my slipper to get his attention, pointing out that Leroy had finally gone to sleep. He and I were on the same frequency. Rising from our beds, we armed ourselves with rolls of tape.

Had we a choice, we would have used fiberglass-reinforced packaging tape for the task at hand, but all we had was white surgical tape, the kind used to hold bandages in place. We worked in silence, gathering more rolls from stashes here and there, meeting up at Leroy's hospital bed.

Leroy was snoring like a grizzly bear while Willy and I worked from above, beside and below the bed, passing the sticky rolls around and underneath the frame, back over Leroy's feet, underneath the bed and over his chest, over his long hairy legs, working quietly lest we wake him up. Before long, we had Leroy taped down good. Back to our beds, we slithered.

Then the drunk woke up. Leroy grew really **angry** about being **taped down** and he started to "**Hulk out**" right there in the Hepatitis Ward. Like **Frankenstein's Monster**, he was reefing at and thrashing his restraints, promising revenge on "*all the **mother-fuckin' sons-a-bitches***"—and then two orderlies came in through those familiar double doors, like the Sheriff and his Deputy.

Taking a good look at the very first bed on the right, they stood five feet from the angry red Leroy. Sticky surgical tape stretched the features on his face as he finally ripped himself free from his bed. More profanity aimed at *everyone*, and Leroy was on his way to a quiet place.

With the return of our liver functions and a healthy gain in weight, Willy and I enjoyed a couple of nights out on the city. After passing through the hospital's security gates, we stood curbside waiting for a taxi.

BOOM!! A passing car's noisy backfire split the night air when its driver shifted gears. I was suddenly standing over Willy, the infantryman, who involuntarily hit the deck.

"It's *okay*, Willy." I chuckled. "We're not in *Vietnam*, dude!" My buddy was showing one sign of being a combat veteran: hypervigilance. He could not relax. Willy hit the deck a couple more times that night, despite himself. [I learned all about such conditioning when it came time for my tour of duty, two years later.]

My memory is a little fuzzy about whatever happened to Leroy, but he never came around my bed again—or there would have been war. A guy spends a couple of months in a hospital ward, you can count on at least one trouble-maker out of the forty-eight who'll give him some grief.

Which brings us to the close of this chapter, which ends with my return to duty. Weighing 150 lbs. with a full bill of health, only two months after arriving sick in Japan, my out-processing began in earnest. I don't remember any long goodbyes. The men in the ward were happy to have their strength back and looked forward to getting on an airliner going anywhere. Even Vietnam.

There was one more holdover for all patients after leaving the 106th General Hospital, that was through the Out-Processing Unit, not far away. While operations worked on assigning empty seats on suitable military flights to Southeast Asia, we were housed forty-eight to the barracks and spent our days picking up cigarette butts and raking lines in the dirt—bored to tears.

I was a smoker at the time, but I really didn't like having to pick up anyone else's cigarette butts. Those three "acting" stripes I left behind in Bangkok, so I was otherwise regarded as a Specialist E-4, not an acting Sergeant E-5. I brought the matter to the attention of the Out-Processing Unit's First Sergeant. I showed him a copy of my orders awarding me the rank, and darned if he didn't cross me off all the detail lists until I left. Thank God for small favors!

The last night I spent in Japan, the barracks was full and everyone was edgy about making the next flight, or spending another super boring day around the barracks. *Lights out* was around 10p.m. and most everyone settled in for the night. Nearby, an army staff sergeant in a lower bunk slipped under his covers and before long, began to **SNORE** like **THE END** of the **WORLD!!**

I've never heard such a racket. It came and went during the night, but by two or three in the morning, everyone within earshot was shouting ***SHUT THE FUCK UP!!*** or ***WAKE UP, YOU MOTHER FUCKER!!*** and so on. Then came the boots and shoes, punctuating every other profane word with a black size 12 combat boot or a size 10-EE shoe, hurled with a vengeance.

Nothing fazed the **Snorer from Hell**. By sunrise, most of us were still trying to catch our forty winks, but *the Snorer* rose up refreshed. Several pairs of boots and shoes were lying on top of his army blankets. He lifted them gently away. Swinging his feet out where he could stand up and get dressed, he had to relocate several odd shoes. He was ever the jovial soldier, saying nothing negative about all the footgear on top of him and around him. *The Snorer* was used to it, I think!

It took a few more years for me to realize the Snorer had *sleep apnea*, a chronic breathing disorder caused by a variety of things, including swollen tonsils. Us soldiers didn't have a fancy name for that brand of snoring back then, we just threw our stinking boots at it!

SLACKERS!

Hiller Helicopter Pilots on the Go

Marching in the US Army can get pretty old. But this is how we moved: slow, but orderly. Whenever our pace began to bore our hard-striped DIs (drill instructors), they cranked it up a notch: *double-time*. For a bunch of guys nearing the best physical condition of our lives, this was doable. Fear motivated us.

There was a place, after all, for those who couldn't keep up, and none of us wanted to go there. If a man came into the Army overweight, he got extra PT (physical training) during company break time. "Slackers" was the name given to the incompetent, flabby, *follower-behinders*, and I know that the name stung.

If trainees had to double-time for long—burdened with thirty-pound packs and loaded, ten-pound, seven-ounce, straight-shootin' M-14s—we would soon be gasping for breath. But upon command, we would have to hold our heavy weapons high over our heads as we ran. Some fell by the wayside, but we were commanded to "*Keep moving!*"

Anything to get through Basic and on to flight school, I thought, assuming a big-eared, motorcycle-racing, high school "Okie" could make it that far. The M-14 was so heavy that, by the conclusion of training, I wondered if I would ever be able to hoist it over my head again.

We grew some new muscles through suffering and exertion, and at long last, our DI *smiled*. Just as quickly, his face waned to a frown as he did an about-face to prepare for the arrival of *new meat*.

"**YOU MAGGOTS!!**" he screamed at them.

By the end of our eight-week episode, Fort Leonard Wood had produced three companies of greenhorn infantrymen. Not-yet-ready-for-combat, but we knew several ways to kill a human, and how to march.

If a guy wanted to be an Army helicopter pilot in the mid-1960s to early-1970s—but lacked a college degree to magic-carpet-ride through training as an officer—he had to go the route more than twenty-thousand adventurous fellows like me did: pass the Army's Basic Training, and you're off to flight school at Fort Wolters, Texas, as a WOC: short for Warrant Officer Candidate.

WOCs were also called "cantaloupes" or even "cows," if the unfortunate wanna-be pinned on his WOC shirt collar brass upside down. If your DI felt like shaming the 6th WOC's 5th Flight as ours did just after handing the platoon leader's position over to me, he will. "*You're all a bunch of slackers!*" Mr. Machina screamed in our faces. 5th Flight, slackers? I had two weeks to change his mind, or else.

Off and running before dawn for our five-times-a-day, mosquito-molested cardiovascular workout, we ran in formations of one platoon or more. Posting road guards with flashlights ahead and to the side, 6th WOC would trot by, stomping their boots every fourth beat. **ONE** two three four **ONE** two three four, *ad nauseum*. Once past any traffic, the road guards had to triple-time to catch up with the double-timing herd.

Officers going through the same training were comfortably bussed to their various classes, but us WOCs often marched. In order to get our WOC flight classes through the curriculum in an orderly fashion, we marched hither and yon to Map Reading, Meteorology, Military Science, Navigation, you name it.

Soldiers have been singing cadences since the first armies were formed. The idea is to maintain order, give the lungs a good workout, and hopefully develop some camaraderie among men: *esprit de corps*, that sort of thing. The platoon leader marches to the right of the group and shouts cadences like a wild man:

"**Hut** two three four,
Hut two three four…"

"**Ain't** no use in **goin' home**,
Jody's got your **girl and gone**.
Sound-off – **One, two!**
Sound-off – **Three, four!**
One, two, three, four,
One two – **Three four!**
I don't know but I've been **told**,
This mans' Army is **growing old**.
Sound off! – **One, two!**
Sound off! – **Three four!**
One two three four,
One two – Three four!"

"**Around her neck**, she wore a **yellow ribbon**.
She wore it the **springtime** and the **merry month of May**
And **if** you **asked** her **why the hell she wore it**,
She **wore it for a soldier** who was **far, far away**.
Far away! Far Away!
She wore it for a **soldier** who was **far, far away**."

"Your **left**, your **le-eft!**
Your **left**, **right, left!**
Your **left**, your **le-eft!**
Your **left**, right, **left!**"

"**O**-le-o-le-**an**-der
O-le-o-le-**an**-der
O-le-**o**-le-**o**-le-**o**-le-**o**-le-**o**-**le**-**an**-**der!**"

"**I** wanna **be** an **A-vi-a-tor!**
I wanna **live** a **life** of **dan-ger!**
Am I **right** or **wrong?**
You're right!
Are we **growing strong?**
You're right!

...and the inevitable:

"**Everywhere** we **go**-oh,
People want to **know**-oh,
Who the hell **we** are,
So we **tell** them,
We are the **6th WOC!**
Mighty, mighty 6th WOC!

To help distinguish 5th Flight on the go, a double-breasted mattress-thrasher friend of mine stitched a dandy guidon to attach to our tall flagstaff. The colorful banner sported a fierce-looking eagle clutching a Thompson machine gun in its leathery talons.

The lettering framing the eagle read, "Machina's Gunners." It was so cool! I originally was tempted to have her sew "SLACKERS" in bold black letters—instead of Machina's Gunners—but my comic brain caved in and I went with the former vs the latter.

I'd been marching in this man's Army for three years by the time I soloed, so the Army's everyday marching songs were beginning to wear thin on my creative brain. Bored with the same ol'- same ol', I invented a couple of new cadences, and tried them out on the guys.

Turns out my Flight liked the new stuff. They also had grown weary of the redundant old routines. So, every time we fell into formation and I called the group to attention, they shouted **SLACK-ERS** in unison like a bunch of pumped-up trainees— which turned a few heads around our rigidly uptight compound.

Marching to the mess hall or one class or another, we would sing our new cadences. The lyrics complained of "fifty-fives," the tiny two-seater Hughes helicopter trainers that shorter guys were assigned to, and we openly dissed the famous *whirlybird* OH-13 Bell—the other tall-pilot-flight-training platform.

Being on the tall side, 5th Flight was assigned to fly the rugged OH-23D Hiller, or the "twenty-three," as my new cadence praised the bird. We were proud of our Hillers, and we let the whole world know it:

*"**Oh**, if I **flew**,*
*A **beat-up Bell**,*
*I'd prob'ly **crash**,*
*And go to **hell**!*

*Or if I **had**,*
*A **fifty-five**,*
*I'd wind it **up**,*
*And watch it **dive**!*

*But if I **flew**,*
*A **twenty-three**,*
*Then all the **birds**,*
*Would envy **me**!*

If I flew,
*A **twenty-three**,*
*Then all them **birds***
*Would envy **me!**"*

*[**Hut** two three four!*
***Sound-off** three four!]*

*Everywhere we **go**-oh!*
*People want to **know**-oh,*
***Who the hell we** are,*
***So** we **tell** them,*
*We are the **SLACK-ERS!***
***Mighty mighty SLACK-ERS!**"*
One two three four
*One two – **three four!**"*
Etc.

Our Drill Instructor seemed to get in stride with our flight's new identity and sudden enthusiasm, which was good, because we saw less and less of him at our formations. At the end of my two-week sentence as platoon leader, CW2 Machina called me into his office.

Standing at rigid attention, I dared glance at the man for an instant, then I went *eyes front*. In the brief glimpse, I perceived an infinitesimal smirk on the right side of Mr. Machina's closely-shaved kisser. He slowly slid a coveted weekend pass across his desk in my direction, like royalty.

I leaned over and collected it.

"Thank you, Sir!" I bellowed. A quick salute, and I was gone.

Well done, 5th Flight—and our talented seamstress, Miss *what's-her-name*.

VESTER THE MOLESTER
AKA THE THRILLER IN THE HILLER

Night Cross-Country Flights with the Outspoken

Vester L. Thompson was a Warrant Officer Candidate whom I met while assigned to WOC Class 68-523, Fort Wolters, Texas. This was way back when, and we were being trained to fly "The Truck," our affectionate name for the Army's "*Raven*," the OH-23D Hiller helicopter.

All of us guys with last names near the end of the alphabet somehow got lumped into flying Hillers, unless they were *height-impaired*, whereas the Army squeezed said midgets into tiny Hughes TH-55 "Mattel Messerschmitts," and they were just as happy as we in our trucks.

Vester seemed to be in every class and onboard every bus we candidates rode to the farther-out heliports around Fort Wolters. Candidate Thompson had prior service before getting into flight school, as did I, so it was natural for us "old guys" to hang out together and shoot the breeze.

One more thing Vester and I had in common was our accents. I had grown up in north-central Texas and he was from Louisiana, so we tended to talk through our noses—especially if we were talking to (or about) each other. It seemed natural to call him "*Hillbilly*," among other things.

Somehow Vester and I made it to the point in our flight training syllabus that called for a night cross-country flight of some magnitude. Since our instructors were way too smart to fly with us on such a risky venture, they allowed one of our fellow candidates to occupy the right seat of the Hiller, believing that we would learn something from it, and hopefully keep each other awake.

An assembly took place before takeoff. The Briefing Officer stood before us, fresh from having the morning off and pleased to have his class reach a milestone in training, with zero accidents. Following his summary of weather and hazards-to-flight, we were assigned flying buddies.

I drew Vester. By then, almost everyone called Vester " *The Molester*," poor fellow. Nicknames were something you lived with in the military, and it doesn't matter if you've never molested anyone or if you were called " *Dorky Bingo*" your whole life. Thin skin will get you nowhere.

Having The Molester as a stick-mate for my night cross-country was a relief. I feared I'd get one of the airline or ag pilots in our midst, guys who already had commercial licenses and were just doing their patriotic duty, like the rest of us. They wouldn't be *near* as much fun.

Takeoff occurred near sundown to give us candidates some time to adjust our prying eyes and get on course over Texas' flat, undistinguishable terrain. It also gave Vester time to get his gigantic map folded so he could navigate us safely to places like Desdemona and beyond.

If you've never been on a long cross-country flight over flat, undisguisable terrain at night, I can tell you that it invites conversation. When not switched to the local Unicom frequency,

I selected "intercom" and we pretended to be two idiots, out for a helicopter ride. At night. With no moon.

Without boldly painted names on municipal water towers to navigate by, *pilots* need reassurance from time to time that the ship is on course. And *navigators* need their pilots to agree with their navigating. But neither of us were actually "pilots," yet. So when in doubt, we followed the rotating beacons of our Brothers in Arms ahead of us.

Not being pilots did not stop us from conversing like aviators and navigators, however. Between *Vester the Molester* and *Dorky Bingo*, there was plenty to be criticized concerning our magnetic course versus our true course, the height of multiple transmission antennae in our path, and the amount of thick, hard, bone in one or the other's skull.

It was likely somewhere high over Hico that I touched a nerve, reminding my opinionated navigator that *he* was also a *hick,* so why didn't we land and have some supper with his kinfolk?

Vester was not about to be undone by anybody from Texas and lit into me about my lousy flight control technique, comparing me to a bull in a china closet. In doing so, he bumped the cyclic control with his poorly-illuminated map, jostling said Hiller and giving me cause to describe his ham-fisted paws in highly unflattering terms.

After another colorful discourse on our return leg to Mineral Wells, I faintly heard someone radio, "Hot mic." I glanced at the panel's transmit selector. It was pointing at the radio's Unicom frequency, not the intercom, where it shoulda been! *"Uh oh."*

Somehow, Vester and I made it back to "Miserable Gulch," its Main Heliport. Landing light on, I hovered down long parallel rows of identical, tied-down *Ravens* to our starting point, and shut 'er down. Invigorated by our night-flying experience, we followed several flight-suit clad candidates filing back into the debriefing room.

We were called to attention as the Briefing Officer entered the room. It was the same Briefing Officer who saw us off hours earlier, but he appeared to have had a hard night: a tattered flag after a tornado.

The BO told us to take out seats. His critique was short and sweet. We were all back "…safe and sound. Mission accomplished. *Except for one thing*," he hesitated, looking us over.

"Candidates Thompson and Wingo need to find new stick-mates."

"*Dismissed!*"

CAMPFIRE THEATER

The Cavalry, in full retreat!

Saturday, Nov 14, 1970. Warrant Officer 2nd Class Dennis Freeman and I had the weekend off from Holloman AFB. Our gray army flight suits littered the BOQ apartment floor, many miles behind us. It was my 24th birthday, and we were out to have fun. Try to, anyway. It was a painful anniversary for yours truly. My high school-sweetheart-wife had divorced me one year earlier.

Dennis' marriage had also fallen apart of late, ergo a weekend camping trip for two shell-shocked survivors of the *Lonely Hearts Club*. The canyons near Cloudcroft, NM were our usual camping destination, but it was too cold at 8,000 feet in November for light camping gear.

Having limited options, I suggested we try La Cueva, an ancient natural cave at the base of the Organ Mountains, east of Las Cruces. Strictly for the adventurous, especially at night. There were no campsites there, but I figured we could make do in one of the arroyos that drained the Organs from around the spooky old cave. Two grown men, what did we have to fear?

A story teller in the making, "Denny" had amassed a respectable repertoire of tales. He was shot down flying a Huey in Vietnam, one of his more colorful stories. Most of his outrageous tales were true, but some were clearly myths.

Denny and I swapped stories on occasion, trying to outdo each other. Or at least, out-deliver one another. Among the folktales I knew best were those I had heard in the days of my Mesilla Valley youth: tales of a murdered priest and *"Marta, the Witch."* I had reserved a special story for Dennis on this dark, windy evening.

The wind was truly gusting and it was totally dark when we parked belatedly near the dirt road leading toward the La Cueva trailhead. We stashed Denny's 1970 canary yellow VW Bug where it was least likely to attract attention. No worries tonight, though. There was no one around for miles. With the engine and headlights turned off, we sat listening to the wind buffet the little car and rattle the sage brush.

The patchouli essence that had soaked into the car's upholstery over time was temporarily overwhelmed by a glowing bowl of Cannabis sativa that Dennis shoved in my face and practically demanded I inhale. So as not to disappoint him, I wrecked my lungs and toasted my brain, and handed his pipe back to him.

Properly prepared for the moment, we stepped out into the night. Hanging onto the car's flexible front trunk-lid in the on-again, off-again tempest, we gathered our packs and a flashlight.

Nothing was said between us, such as, *"…maybe we should wait for better weather?"* We were both determined to escape our daily routines, let our short hair down, get smoked out around the campfire. No, neither of us wanted to play the *wind* card. Not tonight.

Freeman donned his familiar black Stetson, adorned with a snazzy leather hatband and an eagle feather. Seldom did he go hiking without his striking U.S. Cavalry-issued beaver-felt hat. The Stetson was a veteran of the Vietnam war, and everyone knows you never disparage a "Cav pilot," nor his dandy hat.

An Arizonan with an American Indian heritage, Dennis was tuned-in to the desert Southwest a bit more intensely than most. He really fit in here. With his Cav hat dipped low in front, he looked like a cross between *Lee Van Cleef* and *Gandalf the Wizard*.

"Are you going to stand there all night and admire my handsome hat, or are we going to go find some shelter?" Dennis asked at length.

"No, and yes!" I laughed, testing my flashlight's beam on his face, wiping out his night vision.

"Touché!" he exclaimed, rubbing his eyes. I grabbed a jug of water and an entrenching tool, and we headed up the trail. We made enough noise in the process to scare off most demons.

Being former Boy Scouts and all, Dennis and I had no desire to set the landscape ablaze, so we carried basic fire tools. We also toted our packs with bedrolls, the tent, and other "necessities" in one exhausting, loaded-down sortie. That included Freemans' ever-present six-string guitar and carrying-case, of course.

Dennis stopped briefly to re-anchor his wide-brimmed hat and take in the dark, overcast sky. The heavens were eerily lacking in their usual display of celestial bodies.

"I'm really stoned," he whined.

"This way," I suggested, taking the lead. I shined the light into the next arroyo we came to, and we clambered down into it single file. We stopped briefly to flex and rest our aching fingers, then onward and uphill through the dry, winding riverbed we trudged.

Within a few minutes, we came to a tree-sheltered "S" turn in the arroyo that simply begged for us to stop. The sandy soil afoot was clean and relatively flat, near-perfect for sleeping on the ground.

The wind seemed to howl around us, but the center of our crude habitat was somehow wind-sheltered.

"Eureka?" Freeman broke the silence. He seemed unsure, setting his bulky load down. Was Dennis having second thoughts?

Voting to put off raising the tent until we got a fire going, we set our packs aside and strolled off together to round up some firewood. Owing as how hardly anyone ever gathered firewood in the area, we found all the dry tinder we needed close by. But reaching into the brittle brush to harvest it made us think twice about rattlesnakes.

"Go away, buzz-worms!" I suggested aloud.

Before long we had a small, energetic blaze going in the center of the "S" turn. The light from the fire projected our squatting shadows onto the five-foot-high walls of the old arroyo, making Dennis' eyes involuntarily dart here and there, thinking he'd seen something. The longer we sat and stared at the fire, the more Denny fretted in silence.

On one occasion a gust of wind blew through our little space, raking sparks out of our diminutive campfire and sending them off into the night. We hurriedly placed more rocks around the campfire as a windbreak, fearing we might set fire to all of New Mexico.

Strangely, the wind subsided after we rearranged the rocks. Freeman talked about playing his ax, but midway through the process of opening the guitar's case, he stopped and loaded up his pipe. We used up the better part of an hour passing the pipe back and forth while nursing the little fire and debating the pros and cons of the tent.

Dennis was clearly uncomfortable, though he wouldn't admit it. He was a bit more "spiritual" than most, I had long observed. Denny was concerned about sleeping in the arroyo. We would have to zip up the tent real snug or we'd be awake all night worrying about snakes, scorpions and such. Dennis nervously examined the overhead tree limbs for low-hanging gargoyles.

In my smoked-out state, I decided it was as good a time as any to dredge up the story I had been rat-holing for the evening's entertainment. Freeman sat an arm's length off to my right, gazing into the flickering flames while I collected my facts and figures. I had heard the story numerous times from my Las Cruces schoolmates.

I began telling Freeman the story of the hermit.

"Historians of the Mesilla Valley record that a well-known eighteenth century hermit-priest came to live and practice medicine in and around *La Cueva*. Agostini Justiniani was an un-avowed sixty-nine year old Catholic priest from a well-to-do Italian family. Many believed he had the power to heal. His followers would seek his counsel and medicinal herbs, traveling to and from his cave by horse and wagon."

"The priest lived alone by choice," I continued. "But he communicated regularly to those who worried about him by burning a signal fire every Friday, letting them know he was okay. And so it went. When his fire went unobserved April 17th of 1869, a posse was sent to investigate."

"Justiniani was found dead, lying face down on his crucifix, a knife in his back. Although the murder was never solved, some believe he may have angered the local natives by proselytizing on behalf of the Catholic Church. Others believed *Marta the Witch* had something to do with his demise."

Feeling my mouth go dry, I glanced at Freeman and took a swig of warm water from the jug. His eyes were fixated on the flickering fire.

"Far out, Wingo," he said softly. *"And this happened just up the hill from here, you say?"*

I nodded in the affirmative.

Dennis squirmed a bit and stared back at me.

"Marta," he said, whispering her name.

"Numerous nighttime sightings of *Marta* had terrorized modern day farming communities," I reminded him. "It was common for cotton and alfalfa farmers to run their tractors in the cool of the evening, with moonlight and the tractor's lamps guiding the way."

"When the floating visage of an angry-looking Marta suddenly appeared, the driver would bail from the tractor and flee, screaming. More than one valuable tractor was damaged after encountering *la bruja*. Word got around. Drivers refused to work at night, and her legend grew."

Done with my storytelling, I zipped my jacket up to the throat and moved a bit closer to the fire, seeking its warmth. Freeman ever-so-slowly closed his guitar case, without having extracted the instrument. He set the case aside and leaned toward the fire. It was getting steadily colder. Time to gather more firewood?

Freeman would later tell of our little camping trip as a sixty-year-old professional story teller, entertaining elementary students. I frankly never heard his version, but my version ends something like this:

As we sat there, half-scaring the shit out of each other, the cutest little Kangaroo rat you could ever envision hopped out of the uphill darkness and came to a stop within a foot of the fire. He spun to his left, paying both of us a curious glance, then returned his gaze to the fire.

A seemingly tame *Dipodomys deserti* was gracing us with an extraordinarily rare visit, in the dead of night, and he couldn't have been cuter had he been animated by Walt Disney himself.

"*Whoa!*" Dennis exclaimed. "*How cute!*"

He no more said that than the tiny rat did a quick 180-degree turn, staring intently into the darkness from which he had emerged. A sudden blast of wind blew dried leaves and a cloud of dust sailing past Freeman, straight over the rat, and into the fire. And the fire went OUT!

The sudden blackness was a shock to both of us. The last thing we glimpsed before the light went out was one terrified little Kangaroo rat, dashing downhill like a streak.

The flashlight came on as fast as we could fumble around and locate it, its bright beam never looked more reassuring. As I was about to expound on our little rodent friend, Dennis piped up.

"Dorce, do you mind if we leave this place, *right now?*

I could see in his eyes that the *Cavalry pilot* was dead serious. He didn't want to trifle about it, neither. To illustrate his fervor, he stood up and began to throw his kit together in earnest. Sensing what it might feel like to have a knife stuck in my back, I doused the hot coals of our campfire with the rest of the water and heaped sand onto the coals with the shovel.

When I laid the flashlight down to shovel dirt, Dennis wasted no time grabbing it and he headed *stage left* in a hasty retreat. I did my best to keep up with him without stumbling, but what a challenge that proved to be.

Once we reached the car, out of breath, and loaded our stuff inside, Dennis seemed to calm down. It was a long quiet ride to my parent's place along the Rio Grande south of Old Mesilla. I remember my Mom and Dad were up late watching some terrible news on the television when we arrived.

Seventy-five people, including thirty-five members of Marshall University's "*Galloping Herd*" football team, had been killed in a terrible DC-9 accident following their game with East Carolina University hours before. The worst sport-related accident in America's history took place when Southern Airways Flight 932 crashed short of its destination in West Virginia, taking with it the University's coaching staff and many prominent West Virginian citizens.

One could speculate about what scared Dennis off the mountain that eerie night, but knowing him as well as I do, he was always a dependable "lightning rod" for humanity.

STUMPED!

Improvising in the Field

One law of nature promises, "What goes up must come down." That might not include a certain outgoing Voyager spacecraft, but it sure as heck applies to those flying helicopters over the jungle. Nature has ways of dealing with incompetence.

My very first international assignment came about during the early oil exploration days of northeastern Peru. On contract to a Peruvian oil company, Evergreen Helicopters air-freighted two Bell 205A-1s and five mechanics to the Iquitos International Airport a day or so ahead of the pilots. The mechanics would keep the mosquitos alive until we got there, I figured.

Our paleface mechanics were so delighted to be 5,000 miles from rainy, foggy Oregon, they cast aside their coarse work shirts to soak up the powerful Peruvian sunshine. The lot was soon sunburned lobster red and beginning to blister. We pilots admired their painful labor from the shade of a nearby S-62, which sat disabled on the tarmac with a shot-up tail rotor.

In due time, our two aerial tractors were assembled and main rotors tracked. Loaded to the gills with a cargo of heavy support boxes, we were soon clattering along, echelon-right, and westbound at 500 feet. We navigated via the mighty Rio Marañon, 160 miles upstream to base camp.

71

"Puerto Amelia," as our riverside jungle camp was known, sported two concrete helipads and a one-ship hangar, in addition to some breezy bunkhouses and a dedicated mess hall.

The heli-drill we supported was drilling away, 40 nautical miles northwest of base camp. This necessitated a daily aerial commute employing both helicopters which we cranked-up at dawn, weather permitting. We were VFR, all the way.

The way it worked out, we had arrived during the monsoon season. Towering walls of thunderstorms came and went twice a day whether we needed to fly or not. This added stress to our demanding aerial mission. We had our hands full keeping up with a backlog of cantankerous sling-loads while dodging impenetrable squalls.

Being the junior birdman in the flock, I was on a rapid learning curve. A month or so into the assignment, I started to get into the rhythm of things. I almost reached the point of believing I could win over the storms and my hardworking Huey would never let me down.

Which brings us to my memorable afternoon in the Oriente. Somehow my sister ship was released early. An hour or so later, I pickled the last heavy net-load of cement from the cargo hook and landed on the "H."

"That's it for today," the dispatcher drawled. "Take Jose back to Puerto Amelia with you." Right as rain, Jose was waiting for me on the wooden catwalk.

Jose was a tall, strong, sinewy man in his forties, one of the senior *obreros* working for Sun Oil. He was attired in the customary white plastic hardhat, black rubber jungle boots, and the ever-present machete. He was otherwise naked except for a simple loin cloth over his tanned physique. Mosquitos appeared in dense clouds, hovering over, under and around Jose, but Jose did not seem to notice.

One passenger, I scribbled on my kneeboard. *No cargo*. Did we need fuel, the dispatcher inquired, absent-mindedly?

At last look, only a couple of cumulus appeared on the horizon toward Base Camp. No sense in needlessly draining the rig's jet-fuel supply, I had been taught. "No," I replied. "We've got enough to get me there, a little extra."

Jose spoke little English, but he flew back and forth with us frequently, so I smiled when our eyes met. I motioned for him to take a seat near the right cargo door and buckle up. Bringing the RPMs back to 100%, off we flew for base camp.

Rotoring along at cruise power, "ops normal." We headed for a hot shower at Puerto Amelia. Halfway there, I began to have doubts. The clouds ahead appeared to be turning from white to dark and a thick down-stroke of lightning made me jump and involuntarily reduce power. I glanced back at Jose, who had seen the stroke. ***BOOM!!*** came the thunder.

As we approached the north shore of the vast, meandering Marañon, my course line disappeared between the nasty storm on the left and the nastier storm on the right. Great, I thought. There goes that *hot shower* idea.

We needed to find a place to land, but there was only the river and the jungle, and the riverbanks were swollen. Slowing down as the rain began in earnest, I descended toward the treetops. Every minute we deviated ate into our fuel reserve. Jose suddenly motioned with his machete, "*Aya!*" he directed me westward, sensing the urgency in our situation.

Lo and Behold, a single hectare of the nearby jungle had been recently clear-cut. It was evident that we were going to be overrun by the storm on the right, and if I didn't find a place to park an expensive machine, I would soon be out of a job.

"*Si, Aya!*" Jose pointed again. "Lo veo," I shouted over the din. *I see it!*

Although large enough to accommodate our 57-foot-long helicopter, the "clearing" was composed of dense tangles of hardwood stumps that had been sawn off about a foot above the muddy jungle floor. '*Oh crap!*' I thought to myself.

One quick glance at the fuel gauge told me I didn't have long to solve the problem. Using my best Spanglish, I instructed Jose to open his cargo door, lean out, look under the ship, and help me "land" the helicopter.

I cannot overemphasize the performance of Jose at this critical juncture in our flight. No one could have done a better job of coaching me lower, over to the left, *now turn the tail the other way, now back a little,* and so it went, until he was satisfied we could put some weight on the skids. As I lowered the pitch, the ship slid a little this way, rocked a bit, groaned a little and slid to a stop.

Jose had done a masterful job of remotely parking our high-skid Huey, unevenly, but solidly, on clusters of leg-sized hardwood stumps. Soon the turbine cooled and I shut her down. We waited for the rocking to begin as the big two-bladed main rotor mast-bumped to a stop in the wind. Then came the skeeters.

It was an honor to have such a competent man onboard my ship, a native Peruvian with the right stuff. We sat silently in the heavy downpour, sharing our blood while hoping the storm would soon pass.

It did. And although I was apprehensive restarting Evergreen's 205 with the nose tilted up and in a left bank, the ship performed as a member of the team, got us home safe, and only five minutes into that ten-minute fuel light.

PHTHIRUS PASSENGERS OVER THE PUEBLOS

Close Encounters of the Worst Kind

By some miracle, my two-month almond frost protection assignment for a very difficult customer was finally over. My copilot and I were on the last leg of a cross country flight to Grants, N.M. Sand Point Helitack was to be my first fire contract in an Aerospatiale Lama.

Joining me for the flight was veteran Lama pilot Ed McCoy. Once we landed in Grants, Ed would be continuing on to Ruidoso in a fuel truck to start up his Forest Service fire contract, flying a 316B Alouette III. Ed was married to a gorgeous redhead, a thousand miles away.

But I was single back then, so it was likely my idea to pay a visit to the noisiest saloon in town our last night on the road. The spacious joint was kind of dead when we arrived. Mr. McCoy and I found a small table some distance away from the loud, colorful jukebox—which was banging out tunes, yet there were no dancers. In waltzed a little blond who was about to change all that.

It was probably the bad taste in our mouths from dealing with a profane customer's son that left us both feeling in need of alcohol. We had to endure hours of his toxic tongue to draw our pay. We could have simply moped about it back in the motel, but the beer and the jukebox told us we'd made the right decision. Then the little blond number came over and asked me to dance.

I was not accustomed to a female "doing the driving." Ed wasn't going to risk *his* neck, but "Blondie" hardly glanced at him. So, what the heck—the dancing began. I tried to ignore the fact that she danced better than I, maybe holding back so as not to show me up? *Rock and roll, baby!*

After a while we came to a hover, then rose to the rafters— eventually collapsing amid cymbal crashes and strobe lights. All of which made us very thirsty. The *cervesas* were beginning to impact my frontal lobes, hammer my hippocampus. "*More beer,*" we shouted above the din!

After another dance, the little gal retreated to the bar for a breather. But she quickly returned, asking me to dance again—with a big smile. I was beginning to like this gal! Ed drank alone.

Before the night was over, my dancing partner and I had gone through a boatload of quarters. We kept the music machine rocking long enough to float Ed right out the door, followed not long thereafter by the little lady and myself. We were feeling no pain; don't remember who drove.

Before you know it, I was at her place—a rambling affair with a large cushy bed, fit for a roving helicopter pilot to crash upon. The dancing was over, but…

In the morning I said *adios* to Blondie. She really wanted me to stick around, but work called me away. Being wed to a hot French helicopter was about all I could handle.

I picked Ed up at the motel and drove to the airport. We teamed up for the preflight inspection, wiped the morning dew off the bubble and started turning Jet-A into a shrieking cacophony. It was nice having a rated pilot along as we headed east toward Grants, giving each other breaks.

This part of New Mexico had always enchanted me with its history and ancient pueblos, so Ed and I shared our own experiences as we whirled steadily onward, only two hours from Grants.

That was when the marching began. It was very personal, this marching. There was suddenly no doubt that my dancing partner had passed along some tiny insects. *Phthirus pubis*, to be precise—a dreaded body louse that prefers to hang around down yonder, living on human blood.

But *my* crabs weren't just hanging around, they were marching. With crampons on!

It was frankly very distracting. Scanning the gauges, I was worrying more about tiny invaders clawing their way into locations I am hesitant to disclose. My cavalier attitude toward barhopping was *history*, I can tell you that.

Getting to a pharmacy was Job One. One in Grants with a helipad would be ideal. (Why am I flying such a slow helicopter when I need a freaking *Gazelle?*)

It was time to inform my copilot of my plight, I realized. "True Confessions—as the Rotor Turns." Time to spread the word. Broadcast it over the emergency frequency, perhaps?

Ed listened carefully and absorbed my situation report. He was peering into my Ray Bans while nursing burnt coffee from a Styrofoam cup. He thought about it for a moment and finally spoke.

"Well, I wondered why you were squirming around," was all he had to say. But there was no hiding the fact that he inched away from me, up against his bubble door—distancing himself from the infestation. (Who knew a two-hour flight could take a month of Sundays?)

THE DUMBEST DOG IN THE WORLD

Boozer

By the time I took pen in hand, sketched his caricature on a 3x5 card and posted a brief message at the General Store, I had given up on "Boozer." My year-old Bluetick Coonhound had driven me crazy for the better part of three months when I finally reached the point of resignation.

I had put my hard-earned money down on ten undeveloped acres of forested land in southwestern Oregon early that summer. I was a happy bachelor pilot, working seasonally at the nearby Siskiyou Smokejumper Base. I was building a small cabin on the ridge overlooking the West Fork of the Illinois River, with the help of my friends.

It dawned on me early on that I needed a watch dog on the property, once I hauled a bunch of tools and the like to the location. There was an eight-sided canvas army tent standing on the ridge by then, my temporary sleeping quarters—and a dry place for things that needed shelter.

No sooner had I put out the word that I was looking for a dog, I was in possession of two very different dogs from two separate homes. Both were mongrels, which suited me fine, having grown up around mixed-breed canines. I figured two might be better than one. I stuck with their given names and the three of us got along just fine.

The dogs took an immediate liking to their woodsy surroundings and conducted themselves admirably, considering the fact that I didn't have to train them. They were house-broke, they came when called, stayed on the property, and barked like the dickens whenever anyone approached.

About a week after adopting these two critters, one of my firefighting buddies belatedly asked if I was still looking for a dog. When I replied to the negative, he acted disappointed, in that his kid brother had an "extra" Bluetick [Canis lupus familiaris]. He was hoping I'd give him a home.

Purebred dogs were not on my *bucket list*, and a third dog might create problems, I gently explained to my friend. He seemed to accept this at face value, and appeared to let it drop. And THEN my friend's brother showed up unannounced the next afternoon, dog in tow.

Yes, the man said he knew that I was no longer looking for a dog. "Roy" explained that he was merely scouting new locations to hunt for black bear. Thought he'd take "Boozer" for a run. While he was at it, he'd look up and down the riverbank for bear sign.

Boozer, he explained, was the youngest in his brood of hunting dogs. He was a fine looking animal, but not inclined to say "hello" nor meet "new" people. I admire that trait in a dog. He wasn't likely to allow any strangers to come calling without sounding his *bugle*.

Roy was a smooth talking son of a gun, evidenced by him leaving a half-hour later without his walking partner. Boozer had made friends with my two mutts by then and they were happily tearing around the rolling estate like they owned the place.

"He'll make a fine watch dog for you, and you can always take him hunting," Roy added over his shoulder as he sauntered on upstream—Boozer's empty leash in hand.

I would find out soon enough that (1) Blueticks are hunters, not watch dogs and (2) Coondogs in general get in a lot of trouble if you don't take 'em hunting. Boozer happened to have the dimmest light of one dozen Coondogs. He was a fine looking Bluetick, though. His former master was a slick operator. I never saw him again.

Things started out well enough after that, but within days, Boozer began to show his true colors. Making a late afternoon grocery run, I came puffing into camp pushing my trusty wheelbarrow loaded with fresh groceries. The dogs had challenged my arrival loudly, making my day.

I left the grocery sacks sitting on the deck and made another run to where the truck was parked, leaving the goods in the care of you-know-who and his two hairy pals. That was a mistake.

Returning to the ridge within a couple of minutes, I began putting the stuff away when I noticed that (1) Boozer was missing in action and (2) a package of fresh hamburger meat had disappeared from the grocery sack! My plans to cook a juicy hamburger steak with diced onion for supper were now moot.

"*Boozer*," I called. (Nothing.) The other two dogs stood near my feet, looking innocent and wagging their tails, waiting patiently for their dinner. "*Boozer, come here!*" (Not a sound.)

Finally I heard faint snorting and gobbling sounds coming from the bushes near the river trail. I investigated. It was Boozer, alright—feasting upon what was left of my hamburger.

"*Bad dog!*" I shouted, snatching the weathered Pilsen rain hat off my head and twirling it in his direction. Off he ran, the last remnants of torn-up white butcher paper clutched in his greedy jaws. Back he came within minutes, sniffing all around for more burger to steal.

And so it went.

When I lectured Boozer about his bad habits, he just gazed at me all hang-dog with those big, sad hound dog eyes of his, looking miserable. Holding no grudges, I took extra precautions after that to keep Boozer from eating me out of house and home. He didn't care much for dog kibble after tasting human food. Boozer didn't know any better. He stank like Granny's outhouse.

Despite periods of inclement weather and waning funds, I managed to erect a modest 10 x12-foot "A" frame cabin on the crown of the ridge by time fall set in. The tent was a thing of the past, and I was living in the unfinished cabin full time. It had a wood stove and was cozy and dry.

My three dogs would join me in the evenings, gathered around the stove. I would heat up the flat-topped relic from 1943 before I groomed the dogs in the light of a kerosene lantern. All three dogs were serious wood-tick magnets and needed a thorough de-ticking every few days.

For the untutored, a fully bloated wood tick is about the size of a mature pea. If released, they are so round they cannot walk for days. But they shrink in time and eventually find another host, unless something or someone interrupts their little game. I was more than happy to do so. I became an expert de-ticker in short order, amusing myself by dropping the bloated buggers on top of the hot wood stove.

Dropping the ticks one at a time onto the hot surface of the stove, the blood suckers would begin vibrating within seconds. First their legs go spread-eagled, and then—*PIFF!!*—The disgusting parasites would rocket off the stove top, propelled by geysers of steam. They were dead-on-arrival, crash-landing in a dark corner of the cabin to suck no more.

The dogs loved the attention I gave them by virtue of the way they lined up for inspection. I was good to my dogs, but being a tick around "Pedo Heights" could get you killed.

With the change in seasons came the steady rain that is so familiar to Oregon. I was grateful to have a roof over my head while I tried to finish the interior of the cabin. This necessitated running my 5-HP gas generator frequently to power the work lights and electric tools. I ran out of gasoline toward sunset one evening, just as the clouds parted and the rain ceased.

Sweating from exertion, I took off my heavy rain gear and left it lying on the deck to air out while I made the half-hour trip to the General Store and back with a 5-gallon jug of gasoline.

When I returned to the cabin, there sat Boozer, chewing large holes in my expensive rain gear! As if I had the money to replace the jacket and rain hat. I began keeping score on Boozer.

Not much later, it got deadly serious between that Coonhound and me. I'll tell you what happened, but it's not pretty. That 3500-watt generator I was telling you about? It was positioned precisely one hundred feet down the hill from the cabin, by virtue of the expensive one hundred foot, heavy duty outdoor power cord I bought for the job. Noise was the issue.

I came home late one evening and had to find my way from my parking spot to the cabin's trail by moonlight. It was always stimulating to walk the 200-foot trail alone at night, knowing there were wild animals about and three dogs waiting to jump me in the dark when I least expected it.

Boozer, for some reason, was not with the other two dogs when I got to the front steps of the cabin. I didn't hear him bugle during my walk-in, neither—very strange!

Although it was late, I needed to fire up the generator and charge two heavy duty 12-volt batteries before I called it a night. So off I headed down the hill toward the power shed. A quarter of the way there, I passed my dimly-lit Bluetick hound, who was too busy chewing my prized power cord into short ugly pieces to look up.

My brain reeled at what transpired before my fatigued Okie eyeballs. The cord was destroyed. Patching the cord would not work, I realized instantly, due to the heavy amp-loads my electric tools pulled. I would either have to come up with a new cord or move the power shed and generator way up the hill, close to the cabin. I could already hear the noise; too close for comfort.

In an instant my pent up anger rose to a sinister level. Boozer had no idea I was on the verge of exploding. He was content to chew on those wonderful copper wires while I neared critical mass in the moonlight under the tall, fragrant pine and cedar.

Not saying a word, I walked on down the hill; a really bad idea was gathering momentum in my outraged noodle. Boozer must pay for the cord! The generator shed came into view. I was hoping to silently fire it up while that flaming idiot of a dog was still chewing on the naked wires!

Clinching my teeth, I bent over with my head in the shed and fumbled with the choke mechanism. I pulled hard on the start handle, anticipating that an electrified Bluetick would soon be lighting up the hillside.

The Briggs & Stratton engine caught on the first pull and roared to life. Turning to see the lightshow, my eyes instead caught the shadowy form of Boozer, who had followed me down to the shed. He stood there with that priceless look on his face—stinking like a bucket of dead frogs, and wagging his droopy tail. I was Boozer's only friend in the whole world.

I know what you're thinking, and rightly so, but I can assure you I never mistreated my critters. To reduce the dog drama, however, I found new homes for the first two dogs. With a sturdy lock on the front door, I decided to switch to three cats in an effort to keep the cabin's field mouse population under control. Boozer was hard to find a home for, but I kept asking around.

It was too bad about Boozer, a high-maintenance dog. He tested my patience to the max. I kept imagining bizarre ways to get rid of him. And then the annual salmon migration came to town.

One of my downstream Smokejumper pals advised me that the salmon had recently run to their spawning grounds not far upstream from our neck of the woods. Dead fish were beginning to float downstream. He owned a big German shepherd who was partial to salmon, so "Mick" suggested I keep Boozer close to camp and be on the lookout for salmonella poisoning.

Sure enough, Boozer disappeared from sight for more than two days. I had begun to think he might not ever return, *goodie goodie*. When he finally did come stumbling into camp, he truly looked like death on wheels. Poor Boozer's ribs were showing and his legs trembled from the ravages of salmonella. I put fresh food and water near his bed, but he hardly looked at it.

Right about the time I began wondering what a veterinarian might charge me to save Boozer from the hands of fate, up the trail came my Lone Mountain buddy, "Doc." He had driven his VW bus down the mountain to see if I wanted to join him on a seven-day round trip to the mountains of southern California to see some good friends.

Gas was cheap in those days, and we were both free to go; except for my unfortunate canine patient, lying on his death bed. I had cooked up a nice pot of chicken soup the night before. It would be a shame to waste good food. The gears in my aching Okie brain began clashing.

Relocating Boozer's bed to a dry spot under a utility trailer, I gathered a bucket of fresh water and set it near him. Next I set down the kettle of warm soup, after carefully removing all the chicken bones. Ignoring me, Boozer laid his head down and sighed loudly.

Hours later, Doc and I are listening to glorious rock and roll, well on our way to Ashland and points south in "Agnes," Doc's well-traveled van. The two of us were good travelling buddies and we would make the 3,000 mile round trip with few hassles. All the time I was gone, however, I couldn't help but believe that Boozer died where I left him lying, the poor beast.

Sure enough, late afternoon a week later, Doc dropped me off near highway 199 and I took the shortcut to my rustic cabin, humping a quarter-mile of bad road with my overnight gear in a heavy backpack. I was apprehensive about what unpleasant scene might await me.

No sooner had I set my right boot on the gravel driveway heading up the hill toward camp, Boozer's loud, nervous bugle cut through the air like a siren, making me laugh out loud and quicken my pace. Calling his name, my harried hound came running, looking healthy as the day I first saw him.

Fate would have it that Boozer and I would spend more "quality" time together, while I schemed to find him a new home. Word of mouth wasn't working, so I tried a new tactic. Employing my old calligraphy lettering set, I drew a fairly decent rendition of his sad Coonhound mug on a white card. Lettering above and below his head, I carefully printed the following message to whoever might see it pinned to the General Store's outside bulletin board:

"**The Dumbest Dog in the World**. My otherwise healthy Bluetick hound needs a new home. He loves to hunt. If interested, please leave a message at P.O. Box…" [etc.]

Amazingly, my confidence in my fellow man paid off in less than a week. A gent we'll call "Andy" posted a letter in my mailbox, saying he'd like to see the animal. In short order I put the two of them together over at my place.

Although neither one of them did a backflip over their brief introduction, I saw some potential for friendship. Andy seemed to be mildly thrilled to suddenly own a real live Bluetick hound for free. Offering him my only remaining dog leash, Andy thanked me, and the two of them departed down the trail together in a uneasy promenade.

A week later, Andy and Boozer were back, looking like they had made a jovial partnership since I last saw them. Andy said he'd been working extra hard training Boozer. Andy had to admit that Boozer wasn't the smartest hound in Illinois Valley. Still, they liked going for walks together and Boozer was learning to heel.

A few more days went by and here came Andy strolling up the trail, alone. He was looking hang-dog, the same way Boozer used to look when he'd been scolded. I knew something was amiss when he handed me back Boozer's old leash. I asked him gently where his walking partner was.

"I took him for a hike down Deer Creek near Grants Pass the other day," Andy began. "Boozer was following so well, I took his leash off." Andy paused, out of breath. "He heeled for a bit, and just when I thought he was all nice and trained, up jumped a deer and Boozer lit off after him."

A long, pregnant silence followed, and although I wanted to say, "*Go on,*" I didn't. Andy swallowed hard, pausing as if to tell me the worst news imaginable. Finally, the rest came out.

"That's it. Boozer took off after that deer like a bullet, bugling like crazy. His bugle grew weaker and I lost all sight an' sound of him. I hollered loud and long, trying to get him to come back. I hiked up and down the riverbed all afternoon, calling and calling. No use."

I didn't know whether to laugh or to cry, saying only, "I'm sorry, Andy. If Boozer comes this way, I'll let you know." I truly did feel sorry for Andy, losing man's best friend after so much hard work and good intentions.

But a man learns from things of this nature. I know I learned something. The best way to tell how good a dog is, is to have a good mutt to compare him to.

THE WORMRIDDEN ROTORS OF WESTERN WYOMING

Having read about the early pioneers of North America, I knew the significance of Jim Bridger and the wilderness named after him. When Evergreen Helicopters sent me to fight a fire there, I was more than eager. When I learned the names of my ground support crew, I grew less eager.

"Chip and Dale" were brothers who our employer took a shine to, so anyone Delford Smith liked enjoyed an unspoken *cart blanche* when it came to how they performed their respective duties. One was an outspoken young aircraft mechanic; the other brother drove the Jet-A fuel tanker.

I knew from barstool briefings that Chip and Dale were real characters. They would *have* to be to work alongside the average war veteran. Evergreen had many veterans flying for them, so it's not like I expected Chip and Dale to suddenly become tame and compliant in western Wyoming.

The flying was tough, I kid you not. A day ahead of our arrival, a yellow-shirted fire crew set up an empty porta-tank on a ridge a couple of miles from a good-sized pond. My job was to fill it and keep it that way while hose-lays served the firefighters way up there. Higher than usual!

The helicopter manager climbed in my Bell 205A-1 to show me important locations (this was before GPS) and fly with me. I dipped a full Griffith's bucket from the right seat of Uncle Del's sleek green and white rotorcraft and headed uphill and into the smelly smoke. *Struggled*, more like it.

My firefighting experience until then was solely in Alaska at low elevations. I was spoiled on low temps and low density altitudes. A bucket full of water had been the normal procedure, but with no wind, it was clear I would have to traverse the rising terrain to climb with such a load.

My helicopter manager was a great guy but we were operating in the infancy of weight-calculation booklets and regulating water bucket volumes in various conditions. There were performance issues when I hovered over the tank—Del's big Bell would bounce around badly.

Finally, we found the right formula and filled the yellow reservoir with zero help from the wind. It would have been nice to have a steady breeze up there, but no. Hours later, we were released to our overnight accommodations, a fine log lodge with a lush, spacious lawn to park our Huey.

Just what I need after a stressful day of flying, I thought to myself, as the helicopter sat running at flight idle for the customary cooldown. Chip and Dale gathered in front of the aircraft, momentarily at rest. Then they noticed the swarm of nightcrawlers emerging from the closely cropped, damp grass.

This was the first time any of us had seen the phenomenon of worms reacting to the rhythm of two large rotor blades rocking the skids at flight idle—something about the 170-rpm "beat" that drove the little buggers into a frenzy.

Which of course triggered Chip and Dale, waiting for any excuse to go into *Ridiculous Mode*. They began gathering up as many squirming nightcrawlers as they could grab, then repeatedly flung the poor *Eisenia hortensii* up into the rotor blades. Such glee on their elfish faces!

At the appointed time, I reduced the throttle to cut-off. The worm-flinging party was over. The instigators chuckled, having cosmetically obliterated Del's shiny helicopter in worm castings.

"I expect a clean ship in the morning, men," I growled as I snatched my hard hat and headed for the lodge. Their gleeful giggles trailed to leaky-sounding whimpers in my wake. [Dawn would reveal the true extent of the debacle, a generous coating of worm guts, just about everywhere.]

Marching through the lodge's grand doors and into the lobby, I was struck by the dramatic scene above the inn's massive bar. A lone barkeep in long-sleeved white shirt, black garter and bowtie polished his silky-smooth log-bar below two of the finest-looking (stuffed) bighorn sheep I'd ever seen. They were ferociously butting heads from atop some gnarly faux-granite boulders.

Not normally into taxidermy, the scene nonetheless took my breath away, so I eased up to the bar and ordered a toddy, trying to drink it all in. My version of a pilot's cooldown?

I was fortunate that day. I had learned how to keep Del's helicopter in the air and get the job done. And I had an epiphany that would come to symbolize working relationships with guys like Chip and Dale. Sheep "A" butting heads with sheep "B" — one was them, and one was me.

DON'T TOUCH MY BAG IF YOU PLEASE, FEDERÁLE MAN!

Testing my Luck to the Max

Flying in from the northeast, four Bell 212s are low-level in trail formation. Yours truly is in the left seat of the second helicopter. A good friend of mine is flying lead. He switches over from our formation's "bullshit frequency" to notify the control tower at Culiacán International of our intentions. "Mike's" Spanish accent is good; but no problem, the tower personnel are bilingual.

"Culiacán Tower, this is "XC-BEI, two miles northeast for landing, flight of four 212s."

Flying for the Mexican Procuraduria—their version of the FBI—we had been on a spraying mission in the windy, high country northeast of Culiacán. There were two spray birds and two "slick" Bell 212s with armed troops onboard, flying as our backup.

On the way back to the airport, we enjoyed the kickass performance associated with being low on fuel and flying along with spray tanks that were bone dry. And then the guano hit the blower.

The Mexican pilot/agent flying with me pointed urgently to our ten o'clock position with a gloved hand. I could see a broad green field before us as I banked left.

"Marijuana!!" "Enrique" shouted over the tactical frequency.

There were a couple of white objects dead ahead, and now that we were closer I could see people toiling around the white objects, which appeared to be tarpaulins. They had been spread out on top of a freshly mowed marijuana field, and the harvest was underway!

Indeed, the perpetrators in the field saw four, federally-marked jet-powered helicopters turn in their direction, and they took off running! The man strapped into the seat to my right was an experienced Mexican anti-drug agent *slash* pilot who quickly radioed the two slick helicopters to round up the would-be escapees and cuff 'em, while the spray ships landed in the plantation near the tarps, in order to harvest the crooks' booty.

Normally I wouldn't land a heavy wind-machine anywhere near a tarpaulin, but as I approached the location low-level, I could see each tarp had a boat-sized pile of freshly harvested marijuana holding it in place. I confirmed it was marijuana by the smell!

My right-seater opened the door as soon as the skids hit the grass. Enrique disconnected his helmet cord, unbuckled, and headed off to our two o'clock, leaving his door ajar. Ahead of him sat a large red metal object, freshly disconnected from an irrigation system. Enrique was determined to confiscate the bad guys' hardware as evidence, and fly it back to the base.

My buddy Miguel was flying the other spray ship. "Mike" landed at our four o'clock position. His copilot ran to assist Enrique in lugging the heavy red water pump back to our ship. Sweating heavily through their uniformed khaki shirts, the two gung-ho agents did the ol' *1-2-3*, and on the third swing, successfully landed the cast-iron pump on the cargo deck of the helicopter.

Sitting there at 100% RPM in the middle of an illegal pot plantation, I felt like a sitting duck. There was no armor on the helicopter and only the copilots carried pistols. Hopefully any bad guys who escaped our grasp are getting the flock out of Dodge—and kissing their harvest *adios.*

The two Mexican agents began grabbing large armloads of *cannabis sativa* from the pile closest to our ship, heaving the marijuana onto empty spaces around my spray tank. When we had a load, they did the same to Mike's ship, gathering hundreds of pounds of the *forbidden weed.*

Enrique was sweating profusely and reeking of cannabis when he returned to the right seat and got strapped in for the flight back to Culiacán International. He had green stains all over his shirt, which he wore with the same pride a firefighter wears a retardant-splattered hardhat and yellow fire shirt, coming off the fire line. When you're on the front lines, you'll get some on you.

"XC-BEI, flight of four, in sight. Wind 200 degrees at 8 to 12 knots, cleared to land."

The control tower agents were used to launching and retrieving our fleet of spray and utility helicopters several days per week, in our on-going "Operation Cooperation," a marijuana and opium poppy interdiction program launched during the Nixon Administration.

Mike landed ahead at the off-load point and sat idling while I took a helipad north of the main runway. The support ships' armed soldiers unloaded three tied-up prisoners. Roughed up, too—from the looks of them. They would spend the night trussed up in a contraband minivan.

It's not like the bad guys didn't know. The Mexican government had declared a war on drugs, and the televisions and radios all over Sinaloa had been broadcasting repeated warnings of the *"grave consequences"* of winding up on the wrong side of the war.

Mike radioed me on tower frequency: *"Dorce, come up victor."*

I switched to our secret VHF frequency and replied to my good buddy, *"Copy, Mike?"*

"You want some of this?" Mike meant the big mound of marijuana piled behind him. Mike was a non-smoker, but he was a very cool customer nonetheless.

To which I responded, *"Affirmative!"* I had only been able to grab a couple of tops while two federal agents unloaded the weed in my ship into the back of a contraband pickup. I used my helmet bag to stash the stash and hovered over to the parking area, along with the other birds.

Mike had a helmet bag full of contraband pot waiting for me when we got back to the Tres Rios Motel. I was grateful, having run out while working in Sinaloa. I knew there were tons of pot around, I just wasn't sure how to get my hands on some weed without getting caught.

I secured the stash in my black overnight bag and left it unzipped so it would dry before it turned to mold. We kept our cabana's screened windows open 24/7, so there wasn't a heavy odor of weed in our room. At least, I didn't notice it.

And then came a break in the action: the feds decided to shut down the spraying operation for a few days, partly in order to identify new targets. During the lull, one of our former Army spray pilots, "Lorenzo," suggested we drive down to Mazatlán and *surf for chiquitas.*

Always ready for action, Lorenzo was ten years my senior and lived like there was no tomorrow. I was single at the time, but Lorenzo only acted like he was single. He was a lady's man and he had a high energy level.

Having access to one of several identical, beige, four-door Dodge sedans that the Procuraduria drove, Loren and I loaded up the trunk for a weekend run to the beaches of sunny Mazatlán. We found the beachside motel recommended by the narcs and scored separate rooms near the shore.

Loren wasted no time getting into his swim trunks and was soon standing at my door, beach towel and tanning lotion in hand. As it turned out, there were a few ladies on the beach to spice up the hunt. I went in search of Miss Perfect, while Lorenzo was focused on "pussy."

When Lorenzo became engaged in social intercourse, I stole off to my room and dug into my black overnight bag. Breaking off a large crusty top, I crushed it and rolled the flower into a knotty torpedo of a joint. It was ugly, but it would work. The bathroom's powerful exhaust fan blew the smoke away, and in an instant, I was feeling just fine.

I regret to report that I don't recall any romantic interludes on this particular diversion, but Lorenzo may have scored. He usually has several drinks to get in the mood, and is on the dance floor cutting a rug as soon as the music starts. A good dancer, Lorenzo was a man on a mission.

I *do* recall the trip back to Culiacán the following afternoon. As usually happens when you hang out with Loren, the two of us were enjoying a mild alcoholic glow when it came time to depart Mazatlán. It's a long, boring drive north to Culiacán on a marginal highway, at least it was back then. Not the smartest thing to do, but I wasn't going to let Lorenzo drive, buzzed as he was.

Anyone driving Highway 15 knows there are sometimes mandatory traffic stops along the way, with well-established pull-outs to facilitate traffic. Sometimes they are looking for out-of-state vegetables that might be carrying an infestation of insects. And sometimes they are looking for precisely what I had in my black bag.

Sure as heck, we were three-quarters of the way to our destination when a portable stop sign appeared in the road ahead. The sign indicated it was a mandatory stop for one thing or another, I wasn't sure because I was hoping we wouldn't run into the same guys that we worked for.

A pissed-off looking inspector walked to my open window and asked the usual, "Where are you coming from, Sir?" He leaned in close to take a big whiff, and Lorenzo and I did not disappoint him. I answered his question in two words. "Mazatlán, Señor!"

The inspector backed away from the car and held up his right hand, signaling to his Big Boss, who was hanging out in the mobile office.

Uh oh, I thought to myself. This guy's going to want to inspect the trunk. When he came around to my door, he didn't disappoint me. The Big Boss leaned down to my eye-level and asked, "Could you please let us see what's in the trunk?" His English was impressive!

I glanced sideways at Lorenzo, who was beginning to wonder why we were stopped. I leaned his way and whispered, "Inspection, pal. Sit tight. I'll handle it."

Taking the key out of the ignition, I opened my door, acting as calm as possible, when I noticed the large caliber handgun hanging on the Big Boss's hip. And lots of bullets! He also had a massive gut, accentuated by a hand-sized, gold belt-buckle, inscribed in great detail.

"Don't you recognize this *car*, Jefe?" I asked the big man in my very best Spanish.

"We are pilots for the *Procuraduría*," (pronounced flawlessly, I must say). "We work for Capitán Loma Lee," I added, fumbling with the keys in my hand, trying to unlock the trunk.

By then, we are both standing behind the Dodge sedan in mention. I have uttered the key words "Loma Lee" to the Big Boss while slowly unlocking the trunk lid, exposing our two bags. Lorenzo's—which look like a tourist's suitcase, and mine—which is unzipped and practically shrieking at the narcs to slap the cuffs on me.

"*Loma Lee?*" the Big Boss reared back at the mention of a close associate in the war on drugs. He looked at me incredulously. "You two fly the choppers?"

"Si, Jefe, we saw him Friday at the airport," I gushed.

"Okay," he said. "No problem." He added, "you may *go!*"

I clicked the trunk lid shut and gave the Big Boss a sharp salute, while the inspector frowned.

And just like that, I was back behind the wheel, feeling the kind of rush one gets by dodging a bullet. I turned to Loren. He said, "Boy, that was *slick*. I thought they were going to *inspect* us."

"That was pretty close alright. I have over two pounds of weed in my bag," I replied, matter-of-factly. A long silence followed, as the beige Dodge slipped into overdrive and the gears in Lorenzo's sobering brain began to churn, weighing our close call with the narcs.

Lorenzo and I didn't partake in any social intercourse after our weekend together in Mazatlán, I am sorry to report. Loren likes his booze but he signed on to spray weed, not *smoke* it.

Some guys just have no sense of adventure!

MAINTAINING THE ASBESTOS NATIONAL FOREST

Were one to levitate out of Josephine County Airport near Cave Junction, Oregon and fly a heading of 328-degrees-magnetic for approximately 16 statute miles, one would come face to face with 5098-foot Pearsall Peak. Although composed of black serpentine rock, the summit weathers to an orange color, making for a stark, prominent landmark, as one approaches with the sun to their back.

At around 4800-feet on the southern exposure of the very same mountain is an old heli-spot that our US Forest Service Rappel Team was dispatched to maintain. "Busy work," since the Kalmiopsis Wilderness—aka *the Asbestos National Forest,* never seemed to catch fire.

Lightning storms? Surely you jest. Arsonists with boxes full of matches to strike? Fortunately, no. We were more likely to get moldy from all the moisture. But busy work or not, we were happy to be afforded a little flight time to get away from the overhead and the airport for a while.

Our Huey-sized Landing Zone was large enough to accommodate our sleek Bell 212, if one happens to have seven strong hands and plenty of tools onboard to help hack out a clearing for one's twirling rotors.

I off-loaded the crew gingerly to one side and gave them a minute or two to lop off several small tree tops before I dared hover toward the rocky LZ. The mid-morning sun was starting to heat things up on the black escarpment—me included—so as soon as my big, fat rotors came to a stop, I noted the Hobbs-meter time and hopped out to socialize.

In doing so, I discovered that the ground all around was very rocky, and the only shade on this side of the mountain was directly underneath my big, fat helicopter. As friendly chatter with the crew turned to quiet, sweat began to pool on my sunlit brow.

Before I could decide what to do about my sunny situation, it was suddenly "break time," and the rappel crew wasted no time gathering underneath the helicopter, like chicks under a brooding hen. Sandwiches were unwrapped, oranges were peeled. This left the pilot with the shady interior of the Bell as a roomy retreat, one which I accepted with some relish.

After all, this was my mobile office. I had some cool books to read. I also had countless buttons and switches to play with. I could entertain myself for at least five minutes before I couldn't stand it any longer, suddenly powering up the 5-way emergency siren— producing a sonic blast which sent just about everyone under the ship head-over-heels from where they sheltered—back into the sunshine, where they belonged?

I know, it wasn't very nice of me, but you can relax. We're not done with the pilot yet.

In the next hour or so, the crew labored further and further away from the ship, hacking and sawing and piling brush. I earmarked the book I was reading and found my way back outside, joking around with the guys as I watched them work.

Which soon got boring and I retreated under the helicopter. I was careful not to recline near the loathsome external speaker that blasted my crew a bit earlier. I'll have none of *that*. I found a comfortable-looking spot and stretched out on the rocks.

As heat tends to work on the weary and unsuspecting, I found myself slipping off into a nervous, sweaty slumber. I was very likely surrounded by tall, beautiful women in my impromptu afternoon dream, and there must have been glittering wheelbarrows full of gold bullion to fill the picture.

I most likely would have gotten around to introducing myself and filling my flight helmet with booty were it not for the sobering and unmistakable sound of a Rocky Mountain rattlesnake, inches away from my right ear.

Nature prepares pilots for emergency situations like this—being caught napping in a snake pit—by giving them lightning quick reflexes. In my case, Nature shot me partway into a sitting position, abruptly interrupted by the bottom of the aforementioned flying machine.

WHAM was the sound as the pilot's size-seven cranium bounced off the rivet-reinforced, hardened aluminum. Ray-Bans and beads of sweat were sent flying, the impact briefly dimming the pilot's lights and making him see stars in the broad daylight.

The righteous payback was punctuated by a manly chorus of near-hysterical laughter all around the helicopter. I quickly came to realize that the crew had discovered a most unfortunate rattler along the perimeter, and you know the rest.

There were no fires that memorable day in September, back when nothing would burn. My logbook for N83033 crept upward a meager 36 minutes for all our effort. It would have been a picture perfect day, had I **not** had such a **knot** on top of my head. My flight helmet hurt like the devil all the way back to *Asbestos Base*.

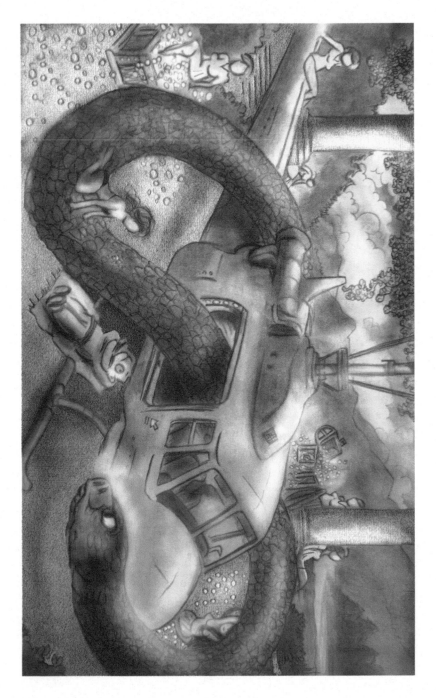

SMOKEJUMPERS VS RAPPELERS

"You'll take the high road and I'll take the low..."

Having moved from California to southwest Oregon recently, I was happily back in my old stomping grounds in the Illinois Valley. I first came here 38 years previously to man a helicopter rappel program on a three-year fire contract with the U.S. Forest Service. The job was based at a small county airport that had been home to the Siskiyou Smokejumpers (SSB) since 1943. The jumpers didn't particularly *want* our helicopter, nor our "rope sliders!"

I flew a brand-new Bell 212 to the base, and from the moment we arrived, I got the feeling we were not wanted. Oh, the jumpers smiled and shook our hands, alright—but I saw the smirks and I heard the grumbling. One jumper "figured out" how much the Bell cost the government for every rotor "wop." "Twenty-five cents!" he shouted. We were in competition, after all, for any wildfires that popped up in the adjacent Kalmiopsis Wilderness.

Trees are majestic in this wilderness. Smokejumpers need 250-foot let-down lines to reach the ground, should their parachutes hang on a treetop. Our rappelers used 250-foot lines, as well. This allowed us to hover-deploy a crew of six into the gaps between Douglas fir and redwood, send down their equipment, drop the ropes—and go for the reserve crew, if needed.

On any distant wildfire, it is a given that jumpers are the fastest and cheapest way to attack. We rappelers figured we were quicker at getting our guys on the ground on fires up to 25 miles away. Beyond that distance, the jumpers' twin-turbine airplanes could get there first and start throwing their streamers. 200 knots vs 100—Aesop's *Tortoise and the Hare!*

My logbook reminds me that we fought only a few fires on the Kalmiopsis our first summer, netting a paltry 35 flight hours in 150 days. My relief pilot fared about the same. Over half of the time logged was our once-a-week practice-rappels.

Things were so slow that I illustrated a highly detailed, full-color smokejumper cartoon book on the side, which grew to fourteen pages. I drew and we practiced. The action was sparse, but I was confident in my rope sliders—er, rappelers—knowing we could compete with the best.

Before the summer was over, the Siskiyou Jumpers and Rappelers would come head to head on the biggest fire of the year. There was a story here, I figured. In order to document the event fairly, however, I needed more than the rappelers' version.

As I began researching, I was righteously called upon to be a docent for tourists at what is now the Siskiyou Smokejumper Base *Museum*. Between visitors, I chanced upon a 3-ring binder titled "SSB Annual Operations Summary" in the old admin building.

I peeked: the August 11th fire was there, alright. Such luck! The fire was written up as "*The Super Bowl of Fire Fighting,*" confirming that it was attacked by fourteen smokejumpers and our twelve-man helicopter rappel team. They misspelled my name!

The fire was 40 miles to the northwest, originating in a logging operation and fanned by 20-mph winds. Its ominous black smoke column was visible for many miles. The jumpers managed to get both of their teams on the ground before I arrived, came to a hover, and threaded six rappelers into a small clearing on the right flank of the fire. Off I went for more rope sliders.

The report went on to say that the SSB "almost lost one jumper" who landed beside the fire. Another jumper hurt his back, striking a stump as he landed. Eleven other jumpers smote the ground safely and quickly unsuited. Double-timing, they stashed their gear nearby and went to work on the fire. According to veteran Gary Cote, one jumper floated over the landing spot.

Few knew it at the time, but before I deployed the second rappeler team, the jumpers had summoned the first crew of rappelers to hustle over to the left flank. The wind had shifted unfavorably and their cache of jump gear was in peril!

I remember seeing my long-faced, ash-coated smokejumper friends the following evening, seated in the local eatery—having some humble pie. They had managed to stop the "Shasta Fire" in two days, then they were bussed back to town with mere remnants of their gear. A twelve-man smokejumper team had been flown in from Redmond as cover.

All these years later, I had hoped to locate other now-retired jumpers in the valley who might give me their account. I yearned for an interview that might make for a decent narrative.

One of my reliable jumper buddies said he had heard that the fire had burned some equipment, but he didn't recall jumping it. Feeling a good story slipping away, my Cherokee scalp started to itch. A polite interval later, I double-checked that Operations Summary—and sure enough, Mr. Reliable was *on* the jump list, the afternoon in mention. He had sailed over the landing zone!

It would be unfair to leave out that the smokejumpers of 1975 depended on the Forest Service approved but antiquated "T-10" parachute, a slightly improved design over its WWII predecessor. Jumpers had little control over their decent and usually came down hard and fast.

All fourteen jumpers had bailed, but my contact steadfastly remembered nothing. Bottom line, the blaze was held to approximately 600 acres. The rappelers returned uninjured *and* with all their gear. On the airborne side, one jumper was sent to the hospital with a back injury. Ten custom-made jump suits and twelve T-10 parachutes had melted into a nylon booger. *Oh, the synthetic stench!*

Maybe *forgetting* is nature's way of dealing with such trauma, and having to call the deplorables for help? For a proud smokejumper, it might have been his worst day in hell—only cooler.

RESCUING THE CELEBRATED M.A.S.H. PILOT...

...a.k.a. "The Battery from Hell!"

Showing up for work at Inland Helicopters one fine morning, I saw the usual cluster of rotary-oriented aviators gathered around an Aerospatiale Lama on the flight line, instead of the customary coffee pot. A long line was laid out around their boots. What appeared to be an aircraft battery waited patiently at the far end of the long line. I saw an urgent look on a face or two. Something was up.

Turns out that our illustrious director of operations, Van Honeycutt, had flown the company's little five-seat FH-1100 helicopter—and a friend—to a remote lake near Grants Pass, Oregon, the previous afternoon, and shut down for a while.

Somehow, as the sun sank, Van's aircraft battery lost cranking power. And with no security for the Hiller, Van and friend were faced with spending the night in the cramped little turbine.

Suddenly stranded, Mr. Honeycutt used his radio to alert Inland's dispatcher as to his predicament, but they were out of daylight by then. Word reached us pilots the next morning, as we showed up for work. There was a gassed-up Lama sitting on the ramp, all ready to go.

Van relayed that there wasn't a good place to land anywhere near the slumbering Hiller. A battery would have to be brought in on a long line and deposited close to the shoreline.

It should be noted that Van L. Honeycutt is a famous pilot. He was one of the medical-evac Bell-47 aviators who flew in the 1970 hit movie, "M.A.S.H.," a cinematic farce about military life in a 1950's field hospital in war-torn South Korea. As Van tells us, the producers liked his name so much, they renamed a character in the "M.A.S.H." TV series, "Honeycutt," in his honor.

A big fellow, Van was known to be rather flamboyant and seemingly always had a torpedo-sized Roi-Tan cigar clamped between his lips. His manly fingers were like skin-covered bananas, making the cyclic control grip all but disappear when he wrapped his huge right fist around it.

Back to the situation at hand, I already knew from round table discussions that none of us pilots had received a lick of long line training. "Vertical reference" was a fairly new skill in those days. And I was the new guy in the flock, having recently hired on. I did, however, have an hour or so with a 100-foot long line: transporting two bodies, over the dark jungles of eastern Peru.

Inland's chief pilot was away on an assignment and out of touch. From the early discussions, it appeared that I had the high poker hand among the potential "rescuers." I figured I could get the job done, and volunteered to fly the battery to Van. No one stepped forward to challenge me. I soon had directions to the lake in mention.

While I strapped into the right seat, my peers saw to the attachment of the load to the long line's swivel hook via a couple of choker-straps, and we tested the cargo hook releases. Before you could say, "*Aerospatiale*," I was headed up and away with the rescue battery.

There I was, flying important cargo like a long-line professional! Elated from finally getting my second long-line mission, I must have been grinning like the *Cheshire Cat*. Added to that, it was a stunning day in heavily-forested southwest Oregon.

The sun was still on the rise as I navigated around a few outlying homes with my external load. The lake in mention soon came into view. I could discern a flaccid Hiller on the far shoreline, and two people standing nearby.

Within a hundred feet from the shore, I slowed to a hover. One of the individuals was a BIG guy, no mistaking Van. They both looked happy to see me, waving their arms like children and pointing to the ground at their feet as my battery's target.

I had been so preoccupied observing details ashore that I allowed my load to disappear under the Lama's belly. Then my rotor-wash hit the calm water underneath me, sending a squall of ripples into motion and disrupting my junior-birdman's vertical reference all to heck!

Pulling a little power to make sure I didn't get too low, I also added a little right cyclic to see if the load would come back into view. Boy, did it ever! The battery shot toward my two-party reception committee like a scene from Edgar Alan Poe's, "*The Pit and the Pendulum*."

The blasted battery swooshed menacingly over the heads of Van and company. They both did a "180" and took off running! My *Battery from Heck* scribed two threatening arcs in the atmosphere before I fought off my ripple-induced vertigo, regained control, and lowered the stupid battery to the ground.

Epilogue: I have to chuckle about my "scary" external load learning experience, but I gladly pass along what I learned that day—and more—to qualified pilots studying Vertical Reference work.

BUSH PILOT!

Have you hugged your driller today?

I didn't realize it at the time, but when I flew a Lama in the seismic boom of the early 1970s, I was taking part in helicopters' Golden Age. Pilots back from the war were finally finding work. They also found new challenges in the way of altitude, weather, and ultimately, one's appetite for working in the Dead Man's Curve. No problem there, I wanted to move those damned *drills!*

New skills were required to airlift all the parts and pieces of seismic work. Precision vertical reference ability was essential for quickly relocating heavy loads. There was logging work to be had afterward for pilots who could handle seismic drills— and the drillers who operated them.

Of the few times I've had to converse with a driller, I noted more muscles than the average worker. They worked hard around heavy, noisy, V-8 engines and drill bits grinding through dense rock—dust shooting out of the hole, covering them from head to foot.

Not the happiest of people, I noted. Oh, you might get a smile out of 'em early in the day but by day's end they were caked in dirt and grease—in no mood to wait for their helicopter ride home. Being freshly married, I knew the joy of returning home to hot chilaquiles.

Which brings us to task on an overcast day in Utah. I had moved the last drill of the day and it was time to fly the drillers in from the mountain. I had dropped two drillers off on a sloping hillside that morning and sure enough, they were waiting for me.

There were very few places to land on this stretch of ground, so we often reused the same spot by necessity. We seldom landed on it more than twice then moved on as the drills progressed.

Descending to land, I could see what looked like my right skid's imprint in the soft soil from that morning. The drillers were crouched just uphill from the imprint, holding onto their packs and hats. I liked reusing an LZ because I knew my rotors would be clear of obstacles without having to check—bushes and the like? I made a smooth landing and waited for the guys to load up.

The dusty duo climbed in and buckled up as I held her steady. Looking back to see if they were ready, one of them leaned forward to holler, "You knew you stuck your rear rotor in a bush back there, right?" I couldn't believe what I was hearing, and I shouted, "*No*, I *didn't* know that!"

We were level enough to shut down, so I did so while wondering where the heck that "bush" came from. After the rotors stopped, I walked aft toward the tail feathers, cursing myself for not looking around, clearing myself as "bush pilots" knew to do.

Sure enough, I landed in a small sage bush. All three blades were green and creased. I had maybe two thousand hours under my belt by then and wasn't ready to make the dreaded phone call to come rescue the drillers and me.

They stayed inside the Lama, too tired to hear any discouraging words. I took a hard look at Aerospatiale's abused blades and decided they would get me back to the staging area. I slid back behind the controls and asked the aforementioned driller, "Is this the same spot I dropped you off this morning?"

"No, we picked a different spot," he drawled. "There was an old pipe stuck in the ground when we got here—so we rolled it down the hill—out of your way." That's what had made an imprint matching my skid.

"Well, they're gonna ground this bird when I land at Service, but I plan to fly it there—and you two would be fools to fly with me." They didn't move.

There was no vibration in the petals to tell me anything was amiss and the short flight to Service was uneventful. Naturally, my mechanic was delighted with my handiwork once I shut down. Had I not been doing such a sterling job, he might have been angry—but he was cool.

Of course, I still had that dreaded call to operations, letting them know I needed three new blades. My bad news was handled professionally, with a warm invitation to come by operations as soon as I got back to Provo. I just so happened to be doing my scheduled ten-day break, but my wife and I would detour to spend some time on the chief pilot's carpet.

The chief wasn't happy with me. Damage to equipment crossed his desk all too often. I didn't try to gloss over damage to one of eighty-eight expensive helicopters in the fleet, I was upset about it too. After a little soul searching, he slid a prepared form across his desk for me to sign.

I was to acknowledge dinging the tail rotor and promise to repay the company for a preventable expense. Even though I couldn't afford to do so, he had his point. So, I signed my life away, went on break, and was more diligent in the golden years ahead.

The good news? Nothing ever came of the form I signed, except that I didn't get fired for <u>not</u> signing it.

THE GOLDEN YEARS

TORBELLINO!

Busted by a Diablo del Polvo

I was elated when spring finally came to the Rocky Mountains my rookie year as a seismic pilot. It was almost warm enough to park my Lama's humongous bubble door during the daytime. Flying door-off in warm weather was the bee's knees. We would reinstall it in the evening to keep out dust, bugs, and larger critters. In the field, you never know what'll sneak up on you.

My mechanic for the job in Utah was a tall drink of water we should call "Slim." A good egg, Slim was strong, capable and confident, which gave me a warm and fuzzy feeling working around him. He was always on the lookout for things that might go wrong, the right kind of man to be maintaining a helicopter. *Safety is no accident,* his philosophy dictated.

As our surface seismic operation moved through the mountains, refueling helispots moved to new meadows or forks in the road every few days. Slim drove our pickup truck fuel tanker, loaded to the gills with tool boxes and support equipment.

Slim's twenty-on and ten-off job required moving to the new location and marking an LZ for me with orange flagging. He would arrive ahead of time and clear the area of any loose articles and be ready to service the Lama on short notice. Slim had no sense of humor, as I recall.

We had experienced just about everything the previous winter, so I wasn't worried about something "new" coming along that we couldn't handle. I should'a been worried.

As the morning progressed, it began to heat up and I figured one more fuel cycle and I'd give the door to Slim, ask him to find a faraway place to secure it until the evening's ferry-back to base camp. After I landed in the new LZ and shut the turbine down for refueling, my trusty mechanic extracted himself from the vehicle, gave me the nod and saw to the refueling.

I remember the weather forecast that day. "Unstable air" caught my attention. It was one of those weird meteorological scenarios when mountain airflow is unpredictable and shit *happens*.

Slim had parked me in a nice grassy area adjacent to a dirt road. My big bubble door was latched during the refueling phase. I made redundant notations in my logbook while eyeballing the fuel gauge. Bringing her up to the 1.5-hour mark, I signaled a thumbs-up.

Done refueling, Slim walked up to my three o'clock, carefully opening the bubble door wide and hanging onto its black metal crossbar behind him with both arms as we shot the bull. I liked the way Slim respected the bubble door. Nothing stupid was going to happen on his shift.

Our attacker approached quietly and invisibly, although we did note a sudden swirling sound at the last instant. Spinning out of the nearby bushes and onto the dusty road, the dirty dust devil grew to a dramatic height, blotting out the sun and making us stop mid-sentence.

Slim held onto the metal crossbar of the bubble door with both hands out of habit, not expecting to be almost sucked off the ground the next instant. Watching helplessly from the right front seat, the powerful "torbellino" tore the fragile door from Slim's beefy grip and wrapped it counterclockwise around the front of the Lama, destroying the door *and* the lower front windscreen in the same instant.

In the ensuing settling of dust, we were practically speechless—having been dealt a rude slap in the face by Mother Nature. One moment it was springtime in the Rockies, the next we were covered in dirt and surveying a sea of splintered plastic.

It was time to assess the damage: just the plastic and our pride. The Lama looked like hell.

Knowing our customer didn't want to hear about any delays, Slim headed for the duct tape while I entered a couple of new squawks in the maintenance logbook. *The boss is never going to believe this*, I thought. Thank goodness I had a trustworthy witness.

When I got back to the Airstream that evening, I described my less-than-dandy day with a dust devil to my beautiful Mexican bride. The descendant of Mexican Indians, her face lit up, saying that we had encountered a *spirit*.

Probably not, I figured. But that *will* happen when I call the Chief Pilot—Mother Hen to over eighty such flying machines—and convey the bad news about his battered bird.

TO PANIC, OR NOT TO PANIC

Flying a Lama with Lulú

So I married a beautiful young lady from south of the border and took her with me everywhere I went, driving to new job sites and helicoptering for a month or so. Then would come a big move, which meant flying the helicopter many miles to the next job site.

Turning our rigs over to our trusty drivers and mechanics to get our trailers there, it was a ton of fun, if you like working in deep snow and ice. There was a bonus: you can take your snuggle-bunny along with you for a little companionship, after putting your Lama to bed at night.

When we met the helicopter at Lava Hot Springs, Idaho, our vintage Airstream was parked all alone in a deserted, muddy RV campground. Ice cold water was squirting ten feet into the air from a tiny leak in the outdoor faucet's pressure-regulator. This mud hole would be our home for two weeks while we finished up a scintillating snowbound seismic survey.

My wife Lourdes ("Lulú") was not a licensed driver at this time in our relationship. She was all alone in the trailer while I was out having a ball, flying low-level, sling-loading seismic gear all over the sunny, snow-covered hills of southeastern Idaho. She told me she was happy making a home for us in her comfy camper, while scanning one or two fuzzy channels on our small TV.

When it came time to move the operation two hundred miles south to our Provo base, logistics required Lourdes be my passenger in the Lama. It was to be her first flight in a helicopter. I remember taking her photo as she sat strapped into the left front seat's four-way harness, all lit up with dazzling Idaho sunlight. She was smiling for the camera, but her hands framed the face of a woman *scared to death*. The rotors were motionless. I hadn't even started the engine.

Rest assured that I talk a good talk when it comes to passenger briefings and how much fun the flight is going to be, heading down the west side of the majestic Rocky Mountains and past the Great Salt Lake. Lourdes drank it all in and agreed to go with me, but she was clearly nervous.

Lulú had two airliner flights to her credit before this, and she was *muy nervioso* both times, she told me. I assured her that I was a competent pilot and I wouldn't intentionally try to scare her. If there were any *problems*, I could handle them. I probably shouldn't have mentioned *problems*.

Lifting off with Lulu a few minutes later, I headed south on a course that paralleled the Interstate to Salt Lake City. By the time I levelled off at about one thousand feet, Lulu was well into what I later learned was a *panic attack*. She was not the same calm person I gave my passenger briefing to only moments before. Lourdes looked very uncomfortable and pleaded with me in Spanish to stop everything and get her back on the ground.

But we were expected in Provo within two hours with the company's helicopter, so I was in *ferry mode* and figured optimistically that she would eventually calm down. I looked to my left. The spectacle of the glorious snowcapped Rocky Mountains was lost on Lulú. She wanted out.

I made sure she wasn't trying to unbuckle (she was too scared to do that) and encouraged her to check out the Great Salt Lake passing slowly by on our right, tourists were bobbing around like corks. Lourdes can't swim, but she wanted out—making me feel terrible for ignoring her pleas.

But you know what? She made it to Provo like so much abused baggage, a little worse for the trip, but a team player for sure. She'll be easier to work with on the next ferry flight, I figured.

Months later, we're halfway through a fine summer helicopter contract based on the North Rim of the Grand Canyon. Lourdes is *with baby* by this time (I have no idea how this happened) and her best friend Dora has flown up from Mexico to visit us in our North Rim campground.

Lourdes was all excited having Dora there with her. The two of them soon hatched a plan whereas she and Dora would fly home to Sinaloa, Mexico for a *big deal* baby shower, then fly her back to me two weeks later. I was delighted to see Lourdes so happy about travelling again.

The nearest commercial airport was on the South Rim of the Canyon. All that was left to do was fly Dora and Lourdes across the awesome abyss in the Lama, a flight okayed by the customer.

I knew Lourdes would take the bit when it came time to cowboy up and climb back into that French flying machine. Dora was up for her first ride and looking forward to it, I could tell. And as much as I would like to write that I was right, I was not. Lourdes and Dora opted *not* to panic.

It was a 260-mile, bumpy-road drive through Lee's Ferry to the airport, for them, thank you just the same. The customer drove them there in a roomy four-wheel-drive truck. The girls left on time for Mexico. Lourdes would be picked up at the airport three weeks later, and driven back to the North Rim, the long way around again.

Lourdes eventually grew to accept helicopters. In the years that followed, she would fly along with me and our three kids. On airliners she was fine. But in helicopters, she was still *nervous*.

TRAINING THE RANDOM ROGUE PILOT

Wind him up...and watch out!

A friend of mine had flown the USFS Independence Helitack contract a few years ahead of me, so I considered myself adequately prepped to flit among and fight fires on the loftiest peaks in the contiguous USA. The helitack crew hadn't changed much since "John" flew a Lama there.

The foreman of the crew was Harold Brown, or "R.C." as he was known: a former rodeo clown. A tough character and fast-pitch-softball ace from Lone Pine, Harold was an old hand to the Forest Service who decided to concentrate on helitack management after a mustang bit the hell out of his pitching hand. "That horse shook me like a rag—my glove saved my hand," he said.

Harold learned first hand (pardon the pun) that a horse has to bite all the way down before his jaw will unlock to reopen his mouth, so the unfortunate rodeo clown can withdraw what's left. How he recovered from that to become a great pitcher is beyond me, but I'm glad he did.

Harold's right-hand man was Jack Sepsy, from the Big Pine, CA Paiute-Shoshone Tribe. Good-hearted, musically inclined, hardworking and—like Harold—he was intimately familiar with every creek and mountain pass to be found on our detailed topographical maps. Expert guides!

On my first day working the contract, I learned that the previous year's pilot was an older aviator who felt right at home cooking breakfast for the crew most of the mornings in his 12-day shift. He was immensely popular with them, ergo the cool reception I got by not stepping up to be the new cook and bottle washer. (I had had enough restaurant work in my previous career, thanks.)

Harold was lining up a training schedule to get me signed off as having had my local area orientation, checking out the steeply rising terrain of the High Sierra to our west and the mysterious White Mountains to the east. You practically needed oxygen to fly to some peaks.

Back at the Independence airport, the wind was blowing like heck, but Jack Sepsy had his new handlers don high-viz vests for the requisite helicopter vector training. They had fancy day-glow light wands to illuminate and dazzle me with. I got suited up, fired up my Artouste turbine and acted intrigued as one marshaller after another took turns directing me in simplistic maneuvers.

During lunch break, the guys and gals produced steel shopping carts and pushed them out to the taxiway where they jumped in— deploying sheets as sails. Exciting races, trust me!

Jack later had the crew practice their hand-signals: lifting up to a hover, hover this way or that, turn right, turn left, take off and land. Pretty boring stuff—unless the pilot spices it up a little.

We had a Griffiths water bucket back then, an orange rubbery cylinder. Harold had pointed out the nearest dip site earlier, a short flight east to hoist 80 gallons from the frigid Owens River.

Most helitack managers would probably have called off training on such a windy day, but I learned that the average day in the Owens Valley brought strong winds, blowing 30 mph and kicking up fine, white alkali dust from numerous dry lakes. Harold had a habit of setting the handbook aside and shooting from the hip. He asked me casually, "Okay with you, Dork?"

For my first water drop, the crew directed me to jettison along the approach end of runway 32. They were standing off to the left, well clear. There was a stiff wind blowing from the west, so I had to offset considerably to hit the paved runway as I flew parallel to it. "*Go back for another bucket,*" RC says. Bucket work is fun, don't you know? I could do this all day long, wind or no.

We were almost done marshalling water drops. "*Just enough fuel for one more,*" I radioed.

"*Put it on the runway and we'll call it a day,*" Jack advised.

Poor RC. Poor Jack. They had considered all the usual factors—except one. They hadn't anticipated the random *Rogue Pilot*. And here he came, diverting well west of them, sailing by forty feet in the air, a perfect height to release his lateral atmospheric river in their direction—drenching the freshly trained, alkali-covered ground pounders.

They stood there motionless for a few seconds, soaking up icy Owens River water and gasping for breath. Their rogue pilot was laughing so hard he had a hard time getting the bird back on the pad—no dry marshaller to be seen. This really was "...*the beginning of a beautiful friendship!*"

GRAND DESIGNS FOR THE GRAND CANYON

When the chief pilot informed me that our mutual employer had landed a six-month contract based in and around the Grand Canyon, I could hardly wait for the other shoe to drop. Yes, I was *indeed* going to be the lucky Lama pilot, contracted to a reputable construction outfit based out of Denver, and ultimately, the National Park Service.

This was fabulous news, for I had been doing some very demanding work elsewhere for more than two years. All the accompanying snow and ice, plus having to move frequently, was wearing me and my Mexican sidekick rather thin. The prospect of having new customers and a warmer climate sounded like manna from heaven.

Naturally, I wanted to set off on the right foot, so I paid special attention to the particulars of my helicopter, my dedicated A&P mechanic, and our trusty support vehicle. My designated helicopter was unfortunately the *Ugly Duckling* in the fleet, but I was delighted to discover she flew more like a swan.

My middle-aged mechanic was missing a few teeth, but I valued his experience. He knew his Lamas, bottom line. The fuel truck had a wheel on each corner and a load of Jet-A. Our chances of making Arizona by sundown were looking better by the minute.

Next came planning the cross-country flight from our Utah base to an improvised construction helispot on the canyon's North Rim. One fuel stop enroute would get me there with a little reserve, and

"Toothless" would drive the fuel truck and meet me at the job site. Only it didn't quite work out that way.

I don't know about you, but I get nervous being assigned a "new" aircraft, especially one with thousands of hours on the airframe. My distrust of unfamiliar flying machinery prevailed, no matter who my employer was. I was especially leery of "new" fuel gauges.

All this wringing of hands leads to my unscheduled landing some twenty miles short of the North Rim that very same afternoon. The Lama's intimidating *low fuel* light convinced me to squeeze the ship into a tiny turnout beside Highway 67, and pray for *Toothless* to drive by.

Which he did, a couple of hours into my cockpit's dusty novel. My mechanic was obviously happy to be back on the road, and soon sent me southbound, brimming with go-juice.

My directions to the construction Landing Zone (LZ) were spot-on. Landing in a grotto of tall Ponderosa pine, a small assemblage of NPS personnel were on hand to welcome me and accompany me to a nearby isolated RV campground, punctuated with white-tailed Kaibab squirrels and giant, fragrant pine trees.

Our personal trailers arrived shortly thereafter, happily my mechanic and I were reunited with our domestic partners. We began hooking up our trailers in the shady retreat. The Lama was not required until Monday, leaving us ample time to unpack, look into the abyss, and act like a bunch of tourists.

We were all warmly invited to attend a "mint julip" party at the Park's permanent housing area the following evening, hosted by the chief Park Service engineer. I was familiar with the featured beverage, but being a beer-drinking individual, I had never sampled the mint julip, per se. My wife didn't drink at all, but she had ladies to chat with while I shook hands all around and tried out a couple of those *delicious* julips.

One would have been plenty, it turned out. The chief engineer was the bartender, so *"the pilot"* was treated to overflowing shots of bourbon [?] while he laid out the more exciting aspects of our upcoming project in the mile-deep canyon, where my skills would be tested.

The party overflowed outside to a gentle slope of green grass, chairs aplenty. My pretty mate was watching, giving me the eye—convincing me lay off those *powerful* julips—and go find a beer, maybe?

When I asked for a beer, the grinning bartender handed me a clean glass and pointed in the direction of the keg. The clever engineers had strategically positioned the beer-on-tap at the top of the incline. I was the first to crack the spigot, unleashing the chilled, frothy, golden liquid—and the tipsy pilot was the first to roll to the bottom of the incline, accompanied by loud hoots of laughter and scattered applause. And yes, I spilt that beer, never tasting a drop.

It was about then that my gorgeous wife rose from her chair—dressed in a lovely black evening dress and several months pregnant—and informed me in no certain terms that she would like to return to the Airstream.

Good thing I didn't make a practice of getting plastered in front of the customer, and it was very clever of the pilot to have *Lulu* along to minimize the damage.

IN A TIGHT SQUEEZE

With a Woman to Please!

The helicopter construction project in the Grand Canyon was a once-in-a-lifetime job I count myself fortunate to have landed. In one summer and fall we built a new caretaker's residence and an impressive trapezoid masonry wall running down the dusty trail toward Phantom Ranch.

The masons building the broad, slab-sided wall commuted daily from faraway Hurricane, Utah every workday in a Suburban full of young, skilled, Mormons who wasted little time talking. The National Park Service showed us where to harvest any rock slabs we needed. A Park Service engineer showed me a hidden little draw east of the project, strewn with slabs we could use.

Flying empty steel baskets to the masons each morning became routine, then hovering loaded baskets back to the wall-in-progress, using Rocky Mountain's SA315-B Lama. The dense 500-million-year-old Navajo sandstone deposits came in several hues of red. The slabs rang like a bell when struck with a hammer—durable as iron, and a treasure to fly around.

There came an interval one morning when the masons needed extra time to gather one last basket of the tombstone-thick slabs. I was not needed elsewhere, so the standard procedure was to shut the Lama down on the Park Services' new helipad and standby.

Taking a portable radio with me, I decided to hike down to the draw where the masons were searching for a few more suitable remnants. After observing the hard-working wall crew for a while, I decided to walk through the downhill portion of the draw and take a look around.

The draw opened into a small box canyon, terminated on the far end by a sheer rock wall. Erosion along the relatively thin wall over the centuries had opened up an interesting void—the missing mass had fallen into graceful deposits of rock debris at either side, creating a window.

After learning I had time to explore a little further, I hiked down into the box canyon toward that dramatic window. I saw no trail or markers anywhere; this was well east of the beaten path for hikers headed to Phantom Ranch. My footprints were the only signs of human activity.

Drawn to the window itself, I estimated the wall on either side to be fifty feet tall. The width of the window interested me for some twisted reason, so I carefully stepped it off from east to west— twice. I then divided my estimate by two and placed a small stack of rocks midway.

It was weeks later that my employer's marketing representative (and an old friend from our army days) came to pay a courtesy call, bringing his pretty wife along to see the sights. It would come to pass that "Mike" asked me to give her a ride in the Lama if the opportunity presented itself.

Mike's wife had French blood in her veins and already enjoyed a reputation of wild consumption and getting naked at parties. I had personally seen her suddenly slurp up a half-inch-by-six-inch slab of juicy ripe mango like a rattler striking a defenseless rodent. So, I was naturally concerned when Mike left me alone with *Mango Woman* to go schmooze the customer.

Once the work crews were moved where they needed to go, the construction foreman gave me his green light to show Mango Woman some highlights of the North Rim. I figured the takeoff from the construction pad out over the first stark abyss would have her squealing—but no.

Down to Roaring Springs, hovering over the pump house project on which we labored. *Yawn.* Back up to some inaccessible Anasazi cliff dwellings where she could see untouched pottery left by the ancients while we hovered within a few meters. *Mango Woman not impressed.*

"My husband was a Cobra pilot," she reminded me. "Can you give me a *real* helicopter ride?"

Fast forward to the little box canyon, coming into view dead off our nose. I see from a distance that my stack of rocks sits right where I left it. Mango Woman sensed what was at hand. "Will *this* thing fit through *that*," she wanted to know?

"A Cobra won't," I answered, giving her a glance. Dropping the nose, the Lama accelerated and zipped through, dead center— Mango Woman screaming, "*OH BLOODY SHIT!*"

I know, I know. I shouldn't have done it. What can I say—a drip under pressure?

Promising to keep our little secret, Mango Woman thanked me profusely once we were back safe and sound on the North Rim helipad and drove off giggling. Relieved to see her go, I was.

Before heading back to the trailer, my postflight included checking all three main rotor blades, making sure no paint was missing off their respective tip-caps. In the interest of safety!

FLYING VAN HALEN

Passenger briefing: Don't start screaming "Jump!"

When the 1983 *US Festival's* huge, untested outdoor stage was ready for mic tests, Western Helicopters got a call from an agent representing the Pasadena-based rock group *Van Halen*. The rep wanted to fly Eddie Van Halen, David Lee Roth and company from our SoCal base of operations to Glen Helen, a measly five-minute flight. A media event? I took their money, booked our new customer and—having nothing better to do, signed myself up as the pilot.

There were four in the group, filling every seat of our Bell JetRanger. After their safety briefing, each performer signed a new "Diver Down" cassette jacket for one of our employees and I loaded them up: three in the back, one in the left front. I frankly found it awkward directing lead singer David Lee Roth into the rear cabin's center seat—his notorious black leather pants had large holes in the side panels, revealing both of Mr. Roth's pink cheeks. A first for me!

Buckling up in the Captain's seat, I was about to hit the Allison's start button when Holes-in-Pants spoke up from behind me: *"Hey! I'm not sitting in the middle. I gotta sit by the window!"* I unbuckle, go around to the left side of the ship. Reopening the cabin door, I facilitated the seat change for the outspoken Mr. Roth—lead guitarist Eddie Van Halen got stuck in the center seat!

The flight to the expansive Glen Helen Pavilion was as short as air taxi flights go. I gave my passengers an obligatory wide orbit from five hundred feet altitude to afford the group a view of the festivals' half-million spectator rolling grass venue, grand high-tech stage, replete with towering speaker stands and powerful spotlights. The hard rock group grew moderately excited.

Landing at one of three secure helipads, I saw the band off to the event's organizer and tied down the Bell for what sounded like one hour of standby before I would fly the group back to Rialto Airport.

I don't know about you, but *standby* is the second-best part of a helicopter pilot's job, if you're not hungry for flight time. Find some shade, crack open a volume of literature—or take a nap.

The stage looked interesting and I could hear mic tests being done. But the extravaganza was a bit too far to walk to, and I didn't really want to leave the bird unattended. Should I dare explore, sure as sunrise "Holey Pants" would reappear, in no mood to wait till someone found his pilot.

My loyalty to the situation became a little fuzzy after an hour lapsed. I allowed myself to venture beyond my standby-comfort zone. I could hear a motorized vehicle beyond the grassy knoll ahead of me. Being a motorcyclist at heart, I strolled toward the sound, glancing over my shoulder from time to time, listening for the whistle of someone coming with holes in their pants.

When I reached the top of the rise, I could see a long-haired young man in dark sunglasses riding the wheels off a quad. The blond rider was alternately standing and sitting on the foot-pegs, absorbing oncoming undulating bumps and jolts with his knees. He exhibited experienced riding technique and I could see his smile from a quarter mile away.

Before long, the off-road enthusiast noticed me watching him and came roaring in my direction. As he got close, I realized it was Eddie again; shirt unbuttoned, decked out in sunglasses—and a broad grin.

Waving as the real live virtuoso Rock Star rolled up, I exclaimed, "I thought you were *working!*"

"Nah," he replied. *"We have people for that. I'm here to ride the QUADS!"* And with that, Eddie spun the agile machine around and flew back across the lush meadow like a happy lark.

He wouldn't keep me waiting back at the LZ much longer, and I flew the group home.

Van Halen was one of the top acts at the *US Festival* in '83, earning a record-setting $1.5 million for the gig. They would go on to release their No.1 hit later that year, *"Jump!"*

It was a real bummer for his one-time-pilot to learn of Eddie's untimely passing in the fall of 2020. I will long remember his ride off into the sunset like an exuberant kid.

THE INFAMOUS MARANA AIRPARK CAPER

Multiple Corporations Evening the Score?

I got my marching orders from the top man at Western Helicopters. "Stormy" was a busy, busy man who juggled a multifaceted helicopter *slash* airplane facility in southern California and more than a score of talented employees, in addition to his large family of smaller storms.

I recall him standing in the doorway to Operations that morning, clutching a thick stack of bills with both hands as he briefed me on a new assignment. Our parent company had solicited our help in "repossessing" two large helicopters from Evergreen's Marana Airpark in Arizona. *Solicited,* as in, "do it." I knew my boss would never ask me to do anything illegal.

This was a headscratcher from the get-go. Higher-level managers had determined that no money was owed to the Arizona space-available company, yet they had their fingers on about $50 million worth of friendly assets-on-wheels.

One of the 3-engined, 24-passenger AgustaWestland EH101 "Merlins" in this caper had gathered dust in our largest SoCal hangar while things cooled down from another corporation's unsuccessful commercial airline operation over Los Angeles several months previously.

Owned by a large outfit, the deciders plotted to ferry the Merlin to Marana Airpark and rent some of that famously arid storage space in one of their humongous hangars. That aircraft was soon joined by a sister ship that had been hangered elsewhere in LA.

Over time, the two birds created a mounting debt for the corporation that had influence over my employers. The deficit grew daily as Evergreen stored, serviced, and worked around the massive rotorcraft. The bill grew to the point that the corporation decided it was time to liberate them, without the courtesy of saying *goodbye*. Calling it a "repo job" made it sound more civilized.

To facilitate the plan, our parent company needed to borrow one of Western's former Naval aviators to pilot one of the Merlins. They would provide the rest of the repo team. Rich Hargis drew some per diem from the accountant, went home to pack an overnight bag, eventually boarding a whistler to Tucson International.

After arriving at the airport, Mr. Hargis was met by the team leader who introduced him to another pilot, hired specifically to abscond with the second Merlin. There were five other conspirators awaiting introduction. They gathered for a detailed conference in adjoining motel rooms with pencils and maps covering the table, making sure everyone understood their job.

Hargis was wisely selected to be the one to seduce Evergreen marketing guru Floyd Helm and his maintenance people into believing Rich and his team were there strictly to perform maintenance on the Merlins. A blue-eyed suave and debonaire sub-hunter in his Navy days, Rich could sell snake oil—to snakes!

Rich volunteered to the Marana folks that both helicopters would need to be towed out to the runup ramp. The rotor blades would have to be installed for their run-ups, therefore both birds would need some fuel. They would buckle things back together and be done by mid-afternoon, following removal of the rotor blades and towing the ships back into Marana's shady hangar.

As part of the ruse, two identical (rented) black Suburbans parked in plain sight of Marana's office personnel. Out climbed two mechanics and two pilots. They had the usual helmets, heavy toolboxes, a case of turbine oil and some clean red shop rags to make them look authentic.

There were three other members of the team sequestered in a nearby location, waiting nervously.

The perpetrators acted like friendly competitors, chatting with Marana's staff whenever eye contact was made, buying Cokes from the bank of vending machines, putting them at ease. For hours they toiled outside under the hot Arizona sun, steadily nearing "T-time."

Looking up from their desks, Floyd Helm's people could see the work going on out on the runup ramp, engines running, blades turning, the visitors' black Suburbans baking away on the dark parking lot. They did not notice when a nondescript rental car stopped just short of the entrance gate, disgorging a driver for each Suburban.

Looking up again from their desks, Floyd Helm's people could see their borrowed tug and towbar sitting unattended as a cloud of dust settled on the runup pads. No mechanics, no toolboxes. Two Merlins in trail formation were climbing, growing steadily smaller northbound—tuned to another frequency, apparently. And those two, hot black Suburbans had vanished like a mirage. *Son of a— gun!!*

Rich returned to report while languishing on Western Operation's plush couch. His delivery described the activities of a jolly comedian. Rich Hargis could easily repo aircraft for a living. I appreciated the fact that we were fortunate to have him around.

It wasn't long before Operation's phone warbled and I was connected to the unmistakable voice of my old pal from our Evergreen days, Floyd Helm, himself. Floyd called to say that he had finally figured out what happened to "his" Merlins. He wanted to comment on our repo team:

"That was pretty slick," he drawled—then hung up.

FLYING MAGGOTS

*"Waiter, a Musca domestica is doing
the dog-paddle in my albondigas!"*

According to my research, flies have been with us since the Cenozoic Era, or somewhere between sixty million years ago and yesterday. Sometime after the dinosaurs kicked off? There is more than one theory on how flies came to be.

I'm not all that religious, but I learned in Bible study many years ago that the scriptures have a lot to say about *pestilence*. It reads in black and white that flies are the fault of the Egyptians!

To summarize Biblical history, it goes something like this: the Lord called upon Moses to threaten Egypt with *"...swarms of flies on them and on their servants...into their houses and on the ground on which they dwell,"* **if** the Egyptians did not let the enslaved population go.

The Lord said unto Moses, *"...stretch out your staff and strike the dust of the earth, that it may become gnats through all the land of Egypt."* So it was written: if anyone outlived the flies, they were *spam-on-the-hoof* for all the gnats that followed.

Traveling a great deal while flying on various missions around North America, Southeast Asia, Peru, and Mexico, I've been bitten by just about every biting bug that flourished there during my labors as a migratory helicopter pilot. I've been chewed upon and desiccated for seven decades!

Aviating through clouds of mosquitos, I've taken a thorough sampling of living conditions in various sectors of the planet. I could testify as to the populations of flies and their biting cousins; ravenous, disease-spreading mosquitos, and precautions to be taken when working thereabouts.

And let's not forget those dreaded late-summer *No-See-Ums*, so small as to be almost invisible, until they **bite.** Then, according to legend, they **crap** in the hole they just made, guaranteeing an infection — the little bastards! *Ceratoponidae* are also called *biting midges.* They fly right through the holes in your socks to chew into your ankles. There's lots of 'em to loathe!

Whack Whack!!

Accordingly, I have come to live in southern California, home to most of the above mentioned flying pests—but in lesser numbers than, say, the tundra of northern Alaska. Bugs around Rialto, California, have a lot of people to choose from, so they are spread thin, just the way I like 'em.

And I hope you will understand why I have no problem dispatching said flying maggots whenever and wherever they might make their unwelcomed appearances. When I was logging with Hueys, I wore a custom ballcap with a laced-leather pigtail built into it. My fly-banger!

Anytime we parked our birds for a few minutes up in Alaska, ravenous, blood-thirsty deer flies would swarm the cockpit and orbit crazily between the instrument shroud and the windscreens. Sitting in the left front seat, I would grab my lethal ballcap and *whack-whack-whack* to lash the cloud of hungry deer flies into an arthropodan slurry, before starting the engine for take off.

In retirement, I toss out my battered flyswatters of old every spring and restock with the latest model, making sure there is a sturdy one in the kitchen, another in the garage, and one or two ready to do battle on the patio. Any fly who comes around my area of operations is asking for it!

As with most stand-up helicopter pilots, I could once *catch* the random pesky fly in one hand, back in my youth. Not very sanitary, but hey: when you're quick, you're *quick!* Now that I'm an Old Fart, my fly-catching days are behind me. I depend on my trusty flyswatter to convey the standing message that I have for all Muscas domesticas and their related brethren: "***Die!!***"

My best fly-swatting days are behind me too, darn it. My measured bat-speed has dropped a few miles per hour, which means I have the tendency to knock flies *out* instead of sending them back to the stinking dog pile they were born in. Metaphorically speaking.

I've learned to hunt down the flies that I knock out before they re-cage their gyroscopes and take off again, an annoyance that keeps happening again and again. ***WHAM WHAM WHAM!!***

Sunning myself out on the patio, I witness the highly isolated incident in which my streaking flyswatter just *barely* nicks a flying maggot, a glancing blow to its stupid little head. Not enough to knock the fly out, but apparently sufficient for brain damage.

Trauma to the airborne maggot is evident: it hovers uncharacteristically like a sweat bee near the point of impact, moving ever so slowly forward. It then hovers slowly straight up six inches or so. Then the fly starts forward again. Then back up six inches or so. Still able to track the sun, the damaged bug is now two-dimensional — and stair-stepping its way to heaven!

Unless of course, Captain Methane intervenes with **Mr. Swatter,** one more time: **_SMACK_**_!!_

"To the **moon**, Alice!"

SAVING TIME!

Or, How NOT to Save Time

My first power line job was a humdinger. The Greg/Helms project was located fifty miles east of Fresno, CA in the Sierra Nevada Mountain Range's Sierra National Forest. Planning began in 1970; the actual work began in June of 1977. Helicopters were a must on this job, helping to build and string the 500KV power line that supported the operation.

The unique Greg/Helms design moves water between an upper reservoir and a lower reservoir. When demand for electrical power is high, water is released from the Courtright Reservoir at 8,184 feet in elevation to the generating station and discharged into the lower reservoir at 6,550 feet. The latter is the Wishon Reservoir.

Three each 400MW generators are put into reverse when demand for electricity is down, pumping water from the Wishon Reservoir back into the upper reservoir to be used as stored energy. PG&E owns this 1,212 MW capacity extravaganza and I was one of several lucky pilots who helped build the power line.

Grateful to Western Helicopter's illustrious chief pilot for having faith in an untrained utility pilot, I put away my smoky fire suits and embraced the idea of stringing sock line for a living.

Pete Gillies was an old hand in the power line trade when he pushed me out of the migrant firefighting nest my wife frankly found intolerable. Being home was essential with children.

The MD500 was a new machine to me, but Pete checked me out thoroughly—including a power off autorotation or two! Before I knew it, I was flying crews up and down the steep, forested terrain to various tower locations, putting in around three fun flight hours a day.

As I became more familiar with things, I started my PLL assignments, flying travelers and long strings of glass insulators into place. Challenging work, but even more challenging for me was relocating the linesmen's long safety-ladders, which were laden with ropes, pulleys, tools and 6-ton hoists. Heavy, the ladders were—and awkward to hook them precisely in the right spot.

But I was taught by the best, and the 500D is such a sweetheart when you break into the saddle, so work was fun. There was enough downtime to relax and see how the linesmen connected the massive steel towers with cool gray insulators and long, twisted, aluminum conductor cables.

The foreman on this job was an old hand, having worked for the utility over 20 years, as I recall. The crew liked him. They felt that "John" had the kind of experience needed to work safely and make big paychecks. The foreman had a way of closing the handbook and doing things his way.

When it came time to "sag" the conductors, John was way ahead of the book. Instead of using a mounted scope and other annoying mathematical steps, he sagged *from the hip*. When he was happy, he gave the word and the expensive conductors were clamped and cut in preparation for jacking the insulators into position.

On and off it would rain, so the toiled earth around the towers grew plush with California poppies and green, sweet-smelling grass. We were about to finish this tower and move.

Then it came time to lower the 6-ton hoists to the ground. The soil was soft enough that John felt it would be safe to "airmail" the hoists from around 100 feet, instead of lowering the gear by hand—the slow but standard, muscle-straining method the crew was so familiar with. So the airmailing began, and John's crew was delighted.

I backed away from the tower in preparation for the first red hoist, and down it came with a vengeance—landing flat with a mighty *SPLAT!!* The hoist from the other arm was next, drawing cheers as it spanked Mother Earth a good one. We were saving time for sure!

The hoists were then sent back out on freshly-equipped ladders to the next tower in line and put back to work. And then it happened. A linesman was jacking insulators into position when his 6-ton hoist broke, sending him flying backward into the waist of the tower, breaking a femur.

Unable to aid him with my little bird, Rogers Helicopters was summoned with their new AStar, piloted by none other than Harry Rogers himself. The stricken worker was flown away within an hour or so, but we were all shaken up by the hoist breaking the way it did.

Time passed. No more hoists were airmailed after that. The sag on all of John's towers had to be redone—they were "off." Inspections on the remaining hoists were performed in retrospect. And John could be found down at the equipment yard—no longer a foreman, and in no mood to talk.

ONE FLEW OVER THE CELERY PATCH

DDDDDamn the FFFFFFrost!

Sooner or later in a helicopter pilot's career, he or she may be called upon to provide "frost protection" over anything from *prunus dulcis* (almonds) to *apium dulces,* aka celery. Faced with forecasts of damaging frost, frantic farmers frequently phone local helicopter outfits to fly or trailer their flying machines there—to rescue the endangered nut of the day.

I can say at this point that I've been there and done that, and it wasn't always fun and games. My very first commercial mission was piloting one of five like-new Bell 205A-1s over hundreds of acres of budding almond trees in central California. It was fun formation flying to get there, meeting with the almond rancher and all, but waiting for some action to happen proved to be frustrating.

We had weeks of lovely weather, spring-like days and nightly temperatures of no concern. We had a routine of washing the aircraft at least once a week and scrubbing the bee crap off the bubbles, but for a bunch of guys who wanted to fly, this drill proved to be exasperating.

Then it happened.

Our first night of frost sent us off into the blackness with a minimum of standing around the warming fire. The anxious rancher radioed from a low spot that he needed two birds down there ASAP, the rest needed to get ready. We fired up the space heaters and unwrapped our cold Hueys.

It proved to be a long night, especially the first hour. Wires that we knew were out there played hard to find. Locating our respective boundaries made for nervous hovering. Were we high enough or too low? Hard to tell. Use the OAT gauge, climb to warmer air and blow it downward—but keep moving. Ooops, a tree goes down!

Hovering around in the blackness, our puny landing lights were inadequate. Thousands of white almond blossoms proved disorienting, swirling around madly in rotor wash.

The rancher had to talk-in one pilot by radio who'd had a hard time staying in his sector, but finally rejoined our hovering herd of Hueys. Embarrassing—we all wanted to do a bang-up job!

We discovered that each aircraft needed mechanical tuning to make our various defrosters and cabin heaters function properly. Windscreens fogged up and bleed-air heaters turned off when we pulled hover power. So when necessary, we rubbed the fog off with shop-towels—dressed like Inuits—or froze our butts off.

After the third night of frost, all of us were dragging ass. It was rough, going from a lazy, no-fly situation to cold weather and flying all night. It proved hard getting to sleep after a long drive to the motel, eating, calling home, and reporting to operations. Once asleep, all too quickly it was time to lace 'em up, eat, and head back to the almond ranch.

The almond season went okay except one of our pilots fell asleep on takeoff and lost his skid assembly, bouncing off the ground. After a harrowing two hours aloft, he was vectored to an Air Force

Base where many sleepy airmen positioned many mattresses to make a bed for the Huey to land on.

The most frustrating frost protection mission I ever flew was near the city of Palm Springs, California. The manager of the celery ranch balked at paying for anything beyond our smallest bird, a 300C used primarily for training. "Bring that one," he said. A man of few words.

My fuel truck driver was working toward his commercial license, so I had ample time to train "Craig" on the finer aspects of staying awake behind the controls until the sun creeps up. A piston-slapper is more of a pain to fly on frost jobs due to having to work the throttle—and having to shut the engine down, vs hot-refueling.

Meanwhile, the plantation's oriental manager was edgy, driving around slowly in his pickup. Was he checking on his celery—or on us?

And so it went. We flew a second night over the celery, getting to know it well. Craig and I were happy to bring up the sun, about to head home in the truck. But no, the ranch manager drove up and said, "That's all, you can fly it home." I was shocked, since the weather forecast called for another night of frost for the entire area. He waved off my concerns and drove away.

The sleep-deprived expression on his face said it all: he was exhausted, half asleep. Forty-eight hours of frost-patrolling his large operation kicked his butt. He was going to bed. End of story?

I said "adios" to the celery patch and flew back to base. Reporting to operations about our unexpected early release, I put things away and drove home to count sheep.

The next afternoon I got another call from the celery plantation, but this time it was the owner. He was unhappy. His crop was a wilted disaster! He wanted to know why I flew home instead of staying on the job.

I hated to deflect blame to his employee-manager, but the owner needed to know why his cash crop had died (needlessly) of frostbite—and lack of sleep.

SPIDERMAN!

I've been called worse

Never have I done more night flying than in southern California, and I'm counting air taxi service to and from scores of airports and heliports, milk runs, pyrotechnic events, mountain rescues, frost protection and rotor blade tracking to name a few. For the most part, I ate these night missions up—though I always had to come "home" to the hangars of *Spider Ville.*

There's something attractive about large, dark hangars in this latitude that black widow spiders cannot resist. In returning to "operations" of an evening (or early morning) I had to enter the company's dimly lit main hangar via the creaky north door, the first vestibule in my path that was dependably occupied by a plethora of *Latrodectus Hesperi.*

I wouldn't be telling this story were it not for my old friend Steve Mankle. He ran Western's auto shop and saw to the facility at our busy operation. Steve reminded me of the night I finally got fed up dodging (and loathing) the nasty hour-glassed arachnids and grabbed my flashlight.

I procured a stout wooden stick about four feet long and duct-taped the flashlight so its beam shined down the length of the shaft. I then fetched a tall green can of Scotch 3M spray adhesive from my office credenza, a premeditated purchase made in anticipation of midnight mayhem.

Starting with the west hangar, I snuck in quiet-like and left the overhead lights off. With the adhesive aerosol can in my left hand, I worked slowly along the wall to my left, shining the light throughout our helicopter rigging inventory—and *Lo!*

Black widow spiders *up-the-butt*, most were waiting patiently above their radiating webs in anticipation of a tender cricket or juicy cockroach. They were not expecting a two-legged searchlight spitting adhesive and carrying a big stick.

Nabbing the first of many bugs in line, I sprayed her and her web liberally and twirled the end of the stick around her in a circular motion—much like the creepy comb-footed arachnid would do, wrapping me up in a cocoon—were I her size.

On to the next victim; I didn't have to go far. The largest of the species were found in corners and along the bases of the walls of the auto shop. Their strong webs resisted my sticky stick to no avail. *Spray-spray-wrap-wrap*—game over. I zapped the little male black widows, too. *Take no prisoners.* No helicopters in here tonight, just hard working field vehicles in need of doctoring.

Somewhere into the second hour of my relentless pursuit of pests, I encountered the late-working, aforementioned Facilities Manager, Steve Mankle. I might have scared him with my *Stick from Hell*, the far end of which had grown to the size of a boxing glove. Like something in a horror movie, it was undulating—scores of little legs signaled for help, reaching out to him.

No time to chat. My wife would be expecting me, but I hadn't eradicated the pests in the large east hangar. There I crouched while weaving around several helicopters that were positioned hither and yon in various stages of maintenance. I still needed to comb the outside perimeter of the complex. Another hour passed—and my boxing glove grew exponentially!

When I reached the tall vertical rain gutter drainpipe at the far corner of the eastern-most hangar, I discovered the Queen of the hoard hiding in the downspout: her hideous abdomen/egg factory resembled a black olive—from sucking up mondo bug juice?

After wrapping up the Queen, I decided to call it a night. But what to do with the *Stick from Hell?* For some reason, I decided to leave it in the paint booth. Blame it on the 3M fumes.

Before scaring anyone half to death the next morning, I checked on the stick to make sure none of my spider victims had escaped. When I opened the door to the paint booth, there stood our stoical Director of Maintenance Bill Dvorak, "admiring" my contribution to his workspace.

Gesticulating with the shaft, I pointed out to Bill how the queen's most prominent leg was waving slowly, like ill-fated Captain Ahab had beckoned to his pursuing whaling boat. Ahab was mortally lashed to the white whale's scarred hide by a web of tangled harpoon lines in the classic *Moby Dick*. I took Bill's countenance as my sign to vacate the paint booth, sick in hand.

Steve, Bill, and I were amazed when I duplicated my catch two short weeks later!

DANCING AT THE COPA

Would you believe the parking lot?

The Sands Hotel of Las Vegas fame was built in 1952 and renovated at least twice in its forty-four-year tenure. The biggest acts in Vegas headlined the Sands' celebrated "Copa Room": Frank Sinatra, Jerry Lewis, Sammy Davis Jr., Dean Martin, and yours truly.

Well, I *did* have a gig at the Sands one night—in the parking lot, at least. Let me explain.

When the *Inns of America* bought the Sands from the estate of Howard Hughes in 1981, a ton of money went into restoring the luster to its draped-balcony exteriors, making its 200 rooms worthy of discriminating guests. The Sands' famed 56-foot sign shone brighter than ever.

When it came time to create the grand opening celebration, the hotel called Los Angeles-based *Tommy Walker Spectaculars.* Tommy "The Toe" Walker and I had discussed pyro-lifting helicopters in his private office once at Angel Stadium. He thought of me when the Sands called.

Walker envisioned a 30 by 20-foot "SANDS" set-piece to be set ablaze above and behind the hotel, spewing a waterfall of pyrotechnic fire below it. The set-piece would be helicoptered into position in the darkness following a Guinness World Records-breaking release of helium-filled balloons, liberated from multiple barn-sized containers on the west side of the hotel.

Singer Sammy Davis Jr. was to be the master of ceremonies for the big gala. Tommy was to work closely alongside Mr. Davis, making sure that everything clicked when Sammy stepped into the spotlights and orchestrated (A) the release of *one-too-many* balloons and (B) the firing of the SANDS set-piece.

Within hours, Tommy and I created a scenario. Our elaborate idea was faxed to the friendly FAA for their okay. A high-profile job like this requires a myriad of phone calls, insurance matters, dealing with fire authorities—and convincing my wife that this was *just another lift job, honey.*

The daylight flight to "Lost Wages" was fast and smooth, the weather for the Gala near perfect. My support crew had a secure LZ laid out in the hotel's east parking lot for my arrival.

I found the Las Vegas FAA to be a gregarious bunch of regulators. Helpful in the planning stages and physically present to inspect things when I landed Western Helicopters' "Easter Egg," a gaily striped 500D model, in the hotel's parking lot. I didn't have to go looking for the field rep—he walked right up with dark sunglasses and briefcase, smiling and ready to help.

As soon as the gentleman was satisfied with my credentials and that of the helicopter, he returned to the casino entrance overlooking the parking lot, where he would watch the spectacle. I connected my 100-foot long-line to the large, rectangular set-piece, festooned with enough flash-cord and pyrotechnics to light up the night.

The plan called for 500,000 balloons to be all boxed up and ready to go. With any luck, the balloons would rise like good helium balloons should and be gone before my 500D climbed into position 500 feet above the parking lot, the set-piece dangling underneath.

I gathered that my gray-haired field representative was nearing his retirement. When my nighttime extravaganza was a wrap, he could drive back to his office and pack up a cardboard box with all his crap and sail off into the sunset.

Tommy Walker needed a dress rehearsal of our external load operation to verify the time it took from engine start to reaching a five-hundred-foot hover. Once that was established, Tommy knew when to signal me. The rest should go as rehearsed, except there would be darkness—and balloons!

The field rep took up a position just inside the entrance to the casino. He could observe the helicopter, sitting fifty feet from the casino, by a flood of lights illuminating our temporary "H." I needed a bright focal point to aid in vertical reference.

Darkness came like a glacier. Finally, it was showtime!

Lifting straight up, I soon detected the field rep outside, craning his neck to watch the Easter Egg climb into the inky evening. My line grew tight and the eight-hundred-pound set piece lifted gracefully, steadied by two long, lateral-ropes, each rope manned by a crew of four.

The dazzling view from three hundred feet above the hotel was distracting. *Focus on the spot*, Wingo. Everything was going along like clockwork, only twenty seconds to reach five hundred feet. Suddenly Tommy Walker keyed his radio, shouting, ***"FIRE THE SET-PIECE!!"***

Mr. Davis apparently got ahead of himself and asked for (A) and (B) *wham-bam*, so I immediately triggered the set-piece's ignitor and tried not to flinch when all that powder lit off underneath me.

It took thirty seconds to burn out, giving me time to rediscover my pupils.

Spotlights sliced through the night as I descended to the parking lot, smelling gunpowder and wondering about the timing glitch. Once the smoky set-piece was on the ground, I hovered to the "H" and began my engine cool-down. But balloons were coming down, toward the ship!

With our friendly field rep frozen in the doorway, one last balloon descended into my spinning rotor system and **_POW!!_** The Easter Egg immediately went into a wild dance, an extreme case of ground resonance! I chopped the throttle none too soon. When the rotors finally stopped, the battered balloon flopped off of one the five rotor blades, onto the pavement.

No harm, no foul. It's a wrap!

The broad smile on a very relieved fed's face was contagious.

FLOGGING THE RACKEN

Strange Things inside Restricted Areas

Weaving in and out of MiG-sized aerial targets stuck in the Utah Test Range's bubblegum soil, I banked my sweet-handling H369 in and out of the honey-combed maze, searching for something. An old fellow at the Wendover Airport said something unique was lying in the dust out here.

Shot full of holes during simulated aerial combat maneuvers, scores of towed, fighter-sized darts had fallen from the sky over the years, driving themselves into northwestern Utah at high speed. These were indeed very strange and unique; but not what I was looking for.

Authorized to operate Western's "Loach" within the restricted area, I was flying a defense contractor around the Great Salt Lake Desert on a two-week mission. We were done for the day; he was helping me search.

Then I spotted the unmistakable form lying on the restricted area's white lake bed. I circled twice around the world's first cruise bomb in my faded pink and white Loach, then landed to inspect the sinister old antique. Hitler's propaganda machine called the very scary V1 a *Racken*.

Racken, it turns out, means *Kingfisher* in German, and if you've ever heard a Kingfisher sound the alarm, you'd understand the similarity to the Nazi's *"buzz bomb."* The bird sings a rapid machinegun-like song, approximating the 50-pops-per-second made by the V1's pulsejet.

The Nazis created some nasty weapons during their Third Reich. The V1 was their cheapest, built by prisoners from nearby concentration camps. Germany sent the V1s toward London guided by a gyro compass hooked to a two-servo control unit and just enough gasoline to reach the target.

Cruising along at three to four thousand feet and 400 miles per hour, the two-ton flying bomb needed only fifteen minutes to reach London from Calais, France. A V1 passing overhead would strike terror into the inhabitants of the British Isles, huddled together in shelters. The pulsejet would suddenly switch off and the weapon would fall out of the sky. Its thousand-pound bomb would lay flat whatever was in its path.

Two years into their use, Allies captured the V1 launch sites. Moving into Poland, the victors were able to seize some operational V1s for research. (Forty-one of them would wind up in museums after the war.)

A few surviving V1s were transported to Wendover after VE Day to reverse-engineer the missile and conduct flight tests. These tests were actually a ruse to hide the USA's new weapon of mass destruction.

Local citizens were tricked into believing the base was doing research on captured V1s, but truth be told, those highly visible launches were mere distractions to divert observers around Wendover from top-secret work being done in and around the hangars at Wendover Army Airfield. The dry lake bed south of Bonneville Salt Flats became my V1's final resting place in early 1945.

As I learned from reading *Project 47* by James L. Rowe, the base's secret mission was to assemble, load, and test-drop inert replicas of the atomic bomb from B-29 bombers over the Utah Test Range. While workers practiced assembling and loading dummy A-bombs, captured V1s were sent buzzing into the air southeast of Wendover, only to be shot down by pursuing P-51s. The ruse worked.

I found it remarkable that our flying bomb had come to rest relatively intact, except for one of its spherical tanks. The sphere came to rest outside the main body of the device, forced through the thin aluminum skin of the fuselage when the V1 crash-landed. The pulsejet's lone spark plug looked odd atop the engine shroud, rusting way. Bullet holes splattered here and there—good shooting!

Climbing atop the Racken in front of its engine, I emulated late Hollywood actor Slim Pickens' cinematic exit from the bomb bay of his B-52 Stratofortress—riding a nuke down to its target. Clamping my legs around either side of the Racken, I slapped the V1's right flank resolutely with my baseball cap, yelling "*YEEEE-HAWWWW*" as my customer preserved the moment with my camera.

Back inside the Loach, we cinched ourselves down and got the big fan going for the flight to Wendover. I likely had a big grin on my face, having crossed a version of *Dr. Strangelove* off my bucket list.

And I regret to report that my prized photo, flogging the Racken, disappeared—like many other strange things are doing out there in the Utah dust.

FLOYD'S FIRST FIRE

The wildfire that BLM (Bureau of Land Management) dispatched me to fight was over two hours away, giving me some time to think as I cruised. After a year of costly avionics work and bucket wiring, the MD500D strapped to my back was on its first ever fire assignment. With an audible sigh, the boss had signed a large check for my brand new Bambi Bucket, and we were suddenly in the fire-fighting business. "Floyd" was scheduled to be my relief pilot, as well.

Upon landing at my Arizona destination's heliport, I wasted no time putting my tanker driver to work on the ship. I then shook hands with the designated BLM Helitack Manager. Once the usual credentials were verified, the manager marked up a fire map for me. Dip sites, wire hazards, that sort of thing. Then his ballpoint pen was all ablur, quickly signing off my load calculation form.

"Hook up your bucket as soon as you can. There'll be no passengers to haul for a while. We have a team of Redmond Smokejumpers working the line. 'Floater' will be your contact."

Moments later, the same manager was outstanding in his clean yellow fire shirt, goggles and a plastic hardhat, signaling me to rise to a high hover. He then sternly launched me toward the distant smoke, bucket in tow.

Switching to the assigned frequency, I was soon in contact with an exhausted Mr. Floater. "We have a creeping grass fire wrapped around the hillside," he sputtered. "Clear of wires for miles around.

171

Wind is light and variable. You'll pass a windmill on the hill with a round stock tank before you reach the fire. Personnel are working the fire line a mile past the tank. We're flogging the flames with burlap. We have no water. Bring your water bucket, over?"

"Oh, I've got a bucket, alright!" I replied, somewhat unprofessionally.

Suddenly, there I was, approaching the best water bucket workout of my whole career. The setup couldn't have been more ideal, as the ambient temperature was unseasonably cool and the water source was situated on a low hilltop. Just right for a 500D. The windmill stood twirling nearby, showing wind direction and cranking up water from deep under the Peloncillo Mountains.

As I sailed by the windmill to dip my bucket, I observed that the shining steel tank was full of clean, cold, water, and it was swarming with a school of wary fish. The "suckers" went crazy when my rotor-wash disturbed the calm surface and my orange and black Bambi Bucket sank to the bottom.

Reefing in full power as I allowed the load to center the aircraft, my bulging 100-gallon bucket rose slowly in a vertical ascent. The water tank's large surface area afforded a degree of in-ground-effect cushion. My trusty turbine was running in the mid-yellow temperature range, producing red line torque. Up we went, flailing and humming loudly, like a seven-bladed Jeep crammed with bagpipers.

Easy on the left pedal, edge her nose forward toward translational lift. Rising steadily to thirty feet or so, I nosedive on down the hill. Reaching 80 knots quickly, I ease off on the power and glide down the gentle slope toward the Smokejumpers with my heavy bag of water dangling.

I knew from experience that grass fires in low-wind-situations are perfect for water bucket work, as we can easily extinguish the fire with a direct hit. The Jumpers obliged me by stepping away from the creeping fire as I approached at speed, aiming the bulging bucket directly at the long trail of flames.

"Right along in there, pilot." Floater advised me. I triggered the release and let 'er rip!

The straining bird rose like a balloon once its load was dumped over the flames. "Good shot, go get some more," Floater pleaded. Music to a fire-fighting pilot's ears, as I did a quick one-eighty back to the tank.

And so it went! There was fire creeping around every hill, and there was more than one stock tank available. A dipper's paradise!

Is Floyd going to like this, I still wondered? He was an FAA Designated Examiner, used to flying two or three commercial check-rides per day. He knocked down some serious income in the process. He'll get all hot and smoky out here. The pay is average, and camp food gets old fast. Floyd's wife is the CFO, too, so she'll not want him dipping around, all over Arizona.

Before I knew it, Floyd arrived to relieve me, helmet in hand. He bought some fire-resistant pro racing boots to try out on his first fire. I briefed him on the daily grind and bid him a fond farewell, fingers crossed. This was my big idea to go fight fires. If this didn't work out, my neck was on the line.

Which brings us to the return of Floyd Hiser, two weeks later. I sauntered on out to the flight line to face the music. Floyd stepped down from his bug-splattered D Model, caked with ash and reeking of prairie smoke and bologna sandwiches. "Damn!" he said. "That's the most fun I've EVER had in a helicopter!" And from then on, it was no problem to get Floyd to relieve me.

DUCT TAPE TO THE RESCUE!

Where would we be without it?

There I was, hovering over the helmeted hooker 250 feet below me. My Huey abided while I held the pitch in check with my left knee. Shifting the cyclic control over to my left hand, I snatched the ever-present sticky roll of gray duct tape from between my seat frame and the radio console with my right hand. With a few practiced movements, I soon had the heavy roll poised to drop out of the bubble window's lower vent hole.

"Don't try to catch this," I radioed as I released the roll to impact close to the soaking-wet worker. (The roll almost always hits the left skid on the way down and tumbles wildly.)

So, what happens when the hooker defies the laws of physics, you might want to know? Broken fingers, dude. Followed by a long walk out of the woods to seek medical aid, while the logging continues, minus one hooker. And four wet hookers can't keep up with a Huey for very long.

But why does the hooker need duct tape in the first place, you may ask? The two most common reasons are 1) to tape up the spaces between their boot tops and rigging pants bottoms to keep the snow out—but most commonly 2) to start a fire!

In a rain-soaked environment, having a warming fire to retreat to during the mid-day lunch break meant *everything* to a tired, hungry woodsman. Whoever had some duct tape was a hero— tearing off a generous strip to light and lay at the base of some kindling. Righteous flames!

My first encounter with duct tape (or duck tape, it's all good) was in Vietnam. Crew chiefs were known to temporarily patch bullet holes in main rotor blades with what the military called "100-mph tape." So we learned to respect it from the start.

Turns out, a lady named Vesta Stoudt is credited with helping promote the use of heat-and-water resistant, pressure-sensitive tape by writing an urgent letter to President Franklin Roosevelt during the course of World War II. Vesta pointed out that soldiers were having to deal with brittle packaging on their ammunition boxes, often delaying quick accessibility.

FDR read Ms. Stoudt's letter and directed the War Production Board to contract with the Industrial Tape Corporation (a Johnson & Johnson operating company) to produce the tape through its Permacel division. Rave reviews followed from the front lines and Ms. Stoudt was credited for pushing this useful material into popularity.

My employer's brow always creased in an unattractive fashion anytime the mechanic ordered a case of duct tape. He was taxed to conceive how our one helicopter operation could go through so much tape! Most of it went into maintaining our long-lines. We had to have two long-lines in operational order, one as a backup. If the lines were shielded by industrial fire hose material, we didn't use as much. But the wires that ran alongside the interwoven cable required mucho tape.

Why did we need a backup line, you might ask? Well, angry hookers have been known to snap the eye of a choker into the remote hook, connecting the hook to a large stump. They then take out their sheath knifes and cut the electrical wires going into the hook.

"Now what're ya gonna do?!" they radio back—if they say anything at all.

The pilot won't be able to pull the stump out of the ground, so he has to pickle the precious line and shut down the logging operation while the woods boss deals with a manpower issue. A separate mission has to be launched to retrieve the long-line, using the backup line with some assistance from the ground.

There's nothing quite as stimulating as flying a 400-foot long-line back to service and coiling it neatly as you land.

So, what was that roll of duct tape doing lying on the floor of my Huey? Well, that's where I inserted my open Dr. Pepper can. It fit neatly into the hole, and the sticky roll stayed put—the best drink holder available that didn't require an FAA Form 337.

Huey logging can be eventful. Logs shift, chokers slip or break, and employment of a technique known as the "Wenatchee Snatch" produces unanticipated G-forces. Which might explain why I landed at service following an exhausting day of logging to discover my Dr. Pepper can had flipped upside down and reinserted itself into the roll of duct tape—sticky liquid flowing everywhere.

My mechanic was *not* impressed.

IN HOLLYWOOD'S SHADOW

The Above-average Logging Pilot

When I learned that "Hollywood" would be relieving me on my Onion Creek logging sale, I did my best to up my production so I wouldn't look bad after he pulled his 14-day hitch. Paul "Hollywood" Bryant was the company's premier Huey-logging pilot, based on weight averages and customer reviews. During job briefings in his warm new Chevy pickup, Paul always made heli-logging sound simple—child's play.

"These logs weigh around 1700 pounds, so take a couple of 'em. Might have to 'rip and tear' 'em out of the slash." He paused to turn up a Seal CD playing in his dash. Long hair to his shoulders, Paul was a handsome pilot. "Too light to haul just one, too heavy to haul three. Eight flight hours a day. Have fun!"

Paul had been around. His father owned a bowling alley in the big city, and Paul could bowl like a pro. But he somehow got interested in driving big rigs, which lead to log trucks. Then came helicopter logging, and his long hauls to and from the mountains gave him the helicopter itch. Paul decided that choppers *had* to be more fun. Cashing in his trucking enterprise, Paul signed up for flight training and never looked back.

The thing about Hollywood? He was a natural. A quick study, he learned to fly in a snap, impressing everyone he came into contact with. Moving up the ladder, he made long-lining a balky remote hook look effortless—one of *those* guys.

Before long, Paul was flying logs all around the northwest, making his hard-working hookers happy with his amazing hook-shots and easy-going manner. Having a cold case of beer waiting for them at the end of the workday, that was Paul's signature.

So everywhere I flew, I was in Hollywood's shadow, like it or not. I began preparing those around me: my talented replacement was going to make me look like an amateur. They scoffed at the idea.

These loggers hadn't experienced the exhilaration of seeing Hollywood come thundering into view two hundred feet overhead, stopping on a dime. His heavy steel remote hook would quickly sail into the picture as though it had eyes, coming to an abrupt stop, two feet in front of your nose. This pilot had the eyes of an eagle and the hands of a surgeon.

One of our impoverished landing rats was trying to put the make on me in front of her jealous boyfriend during this cycle. I assured her she should save her love for Hollywood. *He* was single—*me,* not so much. Her eyes lit up when I mentioned Paul's new Chevy pickup. Her former suitor frowned, fidgeted.

As for my helicopter mechanic, I did my best. He was green. New to heli-logging, he had recently taken a crash course in Huey maintenance. Fortunately, he brought a good attitude to work every day I was there.

To help out my mechanic, I went as easy as I could on his Huey and flew it back to "service" in one piece every night. From there, the mechanic would refuel and slave on his machine for hours, stopping only to consume the dinner I cooked for us on the BBQ grill. He really appreciated my old-fashioned cooking.

Then I went on break. It was two weeks before I rejoined the crew on a burn-salvage timber sale near Omak, Washington. The mechanic on duty was from our outfit's home base, filling in for my previous mechanic. Apparently, Mechanic "A" did not take well to Hollywood or his flying style, coming to the conclusion that his pilot was a showboat who cared more for the landing-rat lady than his helicopter.

Paul didn't make his mechanic dinner, either. And Paul didn't always let him know when the ship was coming in to refuel, often catching him off-guard. Observing Hollywood's heavy-handed style of ripping jack-strawed logs out of heavy slash, frustrations grew.

When the last day of logging came around, the landing-rat lady had her bags packed, ready to leave that night with Hollywood. Her jilted boyfriend gave her the traditional logger's hate-message, a dusty pair of corked work boots, maliciously thrown in her direction.

The last straw for Mechanic "A" was when he climbed atop the Jet-A tanker and opened the inspection hatch to check his fuel level. Hollywood radioed him about that time, advising that the Huey was inbound for fuel.

Not having the hands of a surgeon, the mechanic picked up the radio to respond, only to fumble that expensive multi-channel King FM into the open manway, where it was warmly received by the fancy kerosene therein. It's hard to participate in a logging show if you don't have a radio, so he quit.

Paul went on to log in western Montana. His luck ran out early one warm June morning in 2003, hauling his fifth turn of the day. A component in his tail rotor failed, sending him crashing into tall, unforgiving timber. Word quickly spread throughout the northwest that fateful day; *Hollywood* had pulled his last turn. Logging not far away, I was crushed to learn of his demise. Though I may have been luckier in love, I knew that if I lived to be a hundred, I would never be the logging pilot Paul Bryant was.

SHOT DOWN BY AN IDJIT

A Pressurized One at That, Armed with a Radio!

You know what an "idjit" is, right? Rob the word "idiot" of a syllable, toss in a "j," and there you have your standard *idjit*. A guy would have to **be** one to be working as a heli-logger, according to the insurance companies' short list of hazardous occupations. We're at the top. So my coworkers and I toss such handles around liberally.

BS-ing over the logging frequency throughout the day takes one's mind off the danger and discomforts. Laughing along with your loggin' buddies helps pass the time, especially if you're standing in the snow, freezing—unlike the lucky pilot—who has a 1300-hp heater. We do our best to enjoy the thrills and all-around nut-busting that comes with flying trees around in winter for money.

And anyone who knows me well is aware that, during my tour of Vietnam, I managed to avoid being shot down, or even hit by hostile fire, for that matter. My Skyraider-flying-brother Jon and many of my Huey flying buddies can't say the same. Luck and fate dictates such things in the life of a pilot.

I figured getting shot out of the sky was behind me when I became a civilian. Little did I know, I would be flying logs for a living when it finally happened.

Heading west out of Missoula in the dark, our fragrant Ford service van hummed along the Interstate toward the Clark Fork logging community of Alberton. The thirty-minute commute gave my chopper-mechanic-driver and me some time for a little military mirth, time for the coffee to kick in and the ice to melt off our frosty windows. Heli-logging anywhere near the big city was pretty rare. We relished the alternating current, hot showers and convenience of the KOA while it lasted.

Our timber sale bordered Petty Creek Road, which ran south out of Alberton. Northwest Helicopters' "Super" 204B's landing zone (LZ) was a couple of miles south of town, bordering the road, and was hidden by a tall stand of trees.

As usual, our rig pulled into the LZ ahead of the rising sun. "Jerry" and I would waste no time in un-wrapping our cold-soaked Huey. With any luck, we'd have her warmed-up and ready to haul logs by the time our five-man woods-crew hiked to their uppermost turns and radioed "*Service*" [that's us] to "*Bring it on!*"

N85NW was the vintage Huey I was assigned to, and along with it came trusty field mechanic Jerry Zirnheld, or "Z-Man," as he was known. The same tightlaced former Marine who was confronted by a pissed-off lady logger back in Idaho. "Nena" was wielding a shovel full of dogshit on that cold, dark morning in an earlier episode in the tales of Captain Methane."

My duct-taped *Senior Pilot* logbook [#4 of 4] reminds me that it was the 20th of February, 1998, when *Captain Methane* got shot down. I seem to recall that I got a late start that morning, trying to fire up the bird's balky T-53L-13 Lycoming gas turbine engine.

It wasn't quite dawn when I snapped on my frigid flight helmet and harnessed myself down in order to start the beast. Z-Man was standing twelve feet aft of me—dressed like an Eskimo—with his powerful flashlight focused on the engine. Good helicopter mechanics are always looking for things to go wrong, while humoring the pilot and playing fireman.

A couple of generator-powered heat lamps pre-heated the fuel control unit, fuel boost pumps, and underside of the engine for a few minutes before Z-Man pulled the plug and stowed them away. Battery "on," I depressed the throttle's *detent* button and set the twist-grip *just right*. Flipping the *main* and *start* fuel switches to the "on" position, I yelled "*CLEAR*" like I meant it.

I then triggered the left collective's starter switch. *Click – click – click* the turbine's ignitors fired, loud enough to be heard above the starter and compressor-whine. The bird's heavy 48-foot main rotor started to turn, ever-so-slowly counter-clockwise.

We were getting enough spark, but the gas producer (N1) was hanging up below twenty percent, typical of a cold engine with partially clogged fuel injectors. When I aborted at 10 seconds, Z-Man bellowed, "*Yeah, let's go to Emergency next time.*" He knew the problem, and it wasn't necessarily our anemic battery.

No stranger to starting Hueys in *cold-mode*, I timed the appropriate starter/generator cool-down interval while Z-Man checked around him for bears and/or wise guys sneaking up on him. As if *clairvoyant*, I heard our outfit's Lead Hooker chime in over his portable radio from a ridge a mile away, "*I don't hear no damned helicopter.*"

Knowing "Jeffro" and the boys would be standing on their roped-up logs with corked boots and beginning to freeze, I wasn't surprised to hear him check in on the BS channel. A stand-up heli-logger, Jeff made most heli-hookers look slow; and he never missed an opportunity to jump in somebody's shit. I radioed our situation, urging Jeffro to *standby* while we dealt with the delay.

Re-checking the throttle-setting, I flipped the engine governor's wedge-shaped knob from *auto* to *emergency* mode, and returned the fuel switch to the *on* position.

They taught us back in flight school that engine-starts in the *emergency* mode are a bit more energetic compared to *auto* mode, as unmetered raw fuel is squirted directly into the hot-end of the engine. It is a non-conservative approach that almost *always* kick-starts the given engine.

To the untutored, the all-illuminating fireball erupting from the L-13's tailpipe in the dark of early morning is enough to cause wide-eyed terror—the likes of which I observed on the bright red face of my trusty mechanic, as he ran screaming past my bubble window—arms flailing, shouting *"Run away!! Run away!!"* while illuminated in the glow of the advertised fireball.

Twisting the throttle quickly to *off,* I realized too late that I had fallen for it. If ever there was a fan of *Monty Python's Flying Circus*, it is Jerry Zirnheld. *The Life of Brian, The Meaning of Life*, etc. He's seen all of 'em, lots of times.

Z-Man was rewarded for making me believe my aircraft was on fire [or Python's *Killer Rabbit* was after him] with our second aborted start of the morning. I kept the starter engaged for a few extra seconds to help cool down the engine. This produced an apology from Z-Man—knowing full well that he shouldn't have pulled such a prank!

Consulting the military "Dash 10" [operator's manual] for something like a 25-minute cool-down interval following a second attempt, I radioed the bad news to Jeffro. After a pregnant silence, he keyed his mike and spoke slowly: *"I'll wait here."*

Jeff's sarcasm dripped into his "bitch-mike." But along with his dramatic delivery, I could tell he was mildly amused when he learned *why* I aborted the second start.

Amusing Jeffro had become something the whole crew worked hard at during these long logging days. In charge of the hookers and chasers, Jeff was a clever, curly headed guy, tall and lanky. He set the example, seemed to have boundless energy, and hardly ever missed a day's work.

On this fine Friday in February, we would harvest 384,962 lbs. of western Montana timber in a total of 155 turns, the last of which was Jeffro's. It was a long, drawn-out affair, and when I got shot down, the fallout from the turn obliterated the Log Landing.

65,000 lbs. per hour was typical of the production we fought so hard for on the dreaded *"Friar Tuck"* logging sale. Our agreement with local forestry officials hinged on removing a butt-load of smaller "re-prod" trees from steep terrain, thereby thinning the standing growth for a higher sustained yield.

There was said to be enough good wood mixed in with the *re-prod* to make it feasible, if we worked hard and sent out long, complicated turns to keep the weights up. We averaged 26 turns per hour that day, so 2500 lbs. was the average turn. With only two "chasers" working the landing, they could hardly keep up coiling all the chokers involved. They didn't have time to BS on the radio, neither.

Setting up a decent turn on the *Friar Tuck* was what they call a *blue-haired bitch*. There were bonuses, tronuses and gypsy-tags all over the place. If any of the tags failed when the helicopter took the strain on 'em, production was screwed, as your large turn fell apart in the pull.

Someone had to have a decent turn ready to fly every two minutes. Jeff was quick to verbally pounce on any hooker who didn't put out a fifteen or twenty-log turn several times an hour.

"*You pussy!*" Jeffro would holler whenever their turns came up "light" or their figure-eight riggin' fell apart.

"*I need a back-up,*" they would wail.

"*I got your damned 'back up.' You been trying to keep a $#*@! warming-fire going, but we're moving too fast for that kind of horseshit!*"

"*Go faster and you'll stay warm the same way I do!*"

(and/or)

"*Go work at the #$@&! landing if you can't do any better than that!*"

Hookers made $2 more per hour than the average chaser. Not many guys liked chasing, but there was ALWAYS a big fire on the log landing.

"*We don't need any slackers down here!*" responded the Lead Chaser. "*And quit sendin' in 'slider-tags,' damn it. You're screwing up the chokers!*"

And so it went.

After a couple of exhausting fuel cycles, I sensed that the hookers were trying to swamp the landing so we would have to shut the helicopter down for a spell. That would give the hookers enough time to set a pitch-stump on fire and warm their frozen digits.

Incredibly, one turn we hauled off the sale totaled 21 logs on 22 chokers. It was so long and complicated that it took "Timber" a full cycle to prepare. When he called for me to come get it with two stringers in the hook, Tim gypsy-tagged the top-most chokers into the eye of each stringer and radioed, "*Clear!!*"

Tim's masterpiece was laid out starting at the top of a sloping ridge. It draped over the east and west slopes of the rocky hogback. The turn went down the hill to the bottom-most logs at the tree line, more than 250-feet in length. Adding to that was my 185-foot long-line with two 35-foot stringers in the hook. I took the slack out of the convoluted macramé of steel-wire-rope and re-prod, and started reefing upward.

Checking for glitches and warning lights as N85NW rose, I maneuvered the noisy contraption slowly downwind. I pulled downwind as far as the nearest standing timber would allow; inching steadily upward, drawing the chokers tight. When the proud old bird ceased to rise, I held the power at 40% torque. Turning into the wind, I neutralized the pedals and nosed the Huey over, peeling the elongated turn off the sloping hillside with airspeed and aft cyclic.

My eyes were quickly drawn to a herd of Rocky Mountain Big Horn Sheep [Ovis canadensis] just getting comfortable on the sunlit east slope's rocky escarpment. As my Huey and twenty-one freshly cut Christmas trees appeared rising skyward overhead, they must have experienced "shock and awe," owing to my intimidating manifestation. Off they raced downhill, in a wild, wooly stampede!

"*Way to go, Wingo. There goes our love-life.*" Jeff roped logs from a neighboring strip and saw the whole thing. Mid-canyon by then and staring down at my 400-foot-long, 3800-lb load, I adjusted power. Calling out the turn's weight, I tried to ignore Jeff as I calculated the timing of my tricky comma-shaped approach to the log landing. "*J.J., you'd better give me some room for this one.*"

"*Copy that*," the lead Chaser wheezed. Lunch break came after cleaning up this humongous turn, and coiling all twenty-two flesh-gouging, dirty-damned chokers.

A short flight to the Service LZ followed, where I deftly lowered the remote hook and set it next to Jerry's orange traffic cone.

After a 30-minute lunch consisting of select canned sardines, heated slowly inside my winter jacket the previous cycle—combined with a cup of supermarket coleslaw, Yoplait yogurt and a warm Dr. Pepper. I was good to go for three more cycles!

The hookers ate whatever roots and grubs they could find under rotten stumps and loose rocks. Or so they would have the pilot believe, thinking we might *go easy on them* the last half of the day? Jeff apparently ate a nutritious lunch, though—he never seemed to run out of gas.

Which brings us to what's happening, folks: The third cycle comes around and the guys are dragging butt all over the hillside. The chasers are looking like the *Walking Dead* down there, their warming fire is beginning to wane from lack of attention. The loader operator had a nervous breakdown for lunch but he's still loading log trucks like an angry robot.

Jeff called for his usual 20-drop of chokers, his last choker drop of the day. He began setting out his own work of art, as I took the final turns of imaginative rigging from Ted, Byron and Glen.

Jeff was standing at the top of the ridge near where the sheep had been grazing earlier. I let him know I had him in sight so he would quit waving his "whoopee stick" around like an idjit.

"*Okay, Bingo, come git it.*"

Always a stickler for describing one's turn prior to receiving the remote hook, Jeff instead kept quiet, saying only, "*Pull hard, she'll come easy.*" I lowered the remote hook to shoulder-level.

"*Clear.*" he said nonchalantly, after jamming one lone choker into the hook—and walked off.

Taking the strain on what proved to be the most convoluted turn of the day, I took a quick glimpse at the incredible Montana beauty around my rumbling penthouse in the sky. With the setting sun in my eyes and the ship's nose pointed into the pine-scented wind, I shoved the cyclic forward.

Scanning the critical instruments, I dialed in top-of-the-yellow-band torque. Standing stiff-legged on the tail rotor pedals as the ship shuddered through translational lift, the grand old bird peeled Jeff's monster-turn off the hillside at 40 knots and almost climbing.

The Log Landing was closer at this point in the logging day, requiring that I plan a more aggressive approach with the heavy load. This would lead to a higher-G-load, tighter radius final turn, and it meant that I would have to decelerate radically at the last second in order to flip the bottom-most tags onto the landing.

All the while, I would have to be sharp to power up in time to prevent the large logs in Jeff's turn from smashing everything (and anyone) under them, like *Pink Floyd's* ugly *hammers*.

Seconds after I took off, and right about the time the pilot usually radios the weight of a turn, *someone* unclipped their bitch mic from their chest-pack's shoulder strap. Stretching its pigtail cord to the max by extending the device earthward, he or she placed the mic directly underneath his or her uncovered buttocks.

What followed had to be the *longest, loudest,* most *energetic,* upward climbing and ultimately *over-lubricated* fart ever heard inside a flight helmet.

"*Oh, nooooo!!!*" I laughed and laughed and laughed.

Paralyzed by debilitating laughter and blinded by tears, Captain Methane did his best to stay at the controls and not fall prey to the urge: punch off the whole damned load, turn off the fuel, open the door, and jump the hell out.

"*Clear the landing!*" I shouted to J.J. and crew.

Tears were pooling into both lenses of my bifocals as I heard that fart again in my weary brain. I fought to see where the landing might be; guessing where the bottom-most logs were as they swung around counterclockwise onto the landing—just missing the shell-shocked loader. *Thump Thump Thump, Wham Wham Wham!!* Finally, the whole affair was safely on the ground, and the landing was wiped out, but good!

There was abundant radio chatter subsequent to *being shot down.* Personally, I was reduced to 180-lbs. of babbling jello, barely able to land the helicopter afterward. My poor Okie brain would be replaying that ludicrous fart for hours, and well into my sleep.

By the time Jerry and I got the ship serviced, her rotors tied down and the log book filled out, Jeff himself walked up the road into the Service Landing. He had his familiar dented orange hard hat sitting cocked back on his crazy head, and a big shit-eatin' grin on his face!

STATIC ELECTRICITY AND GOING FETAL

Helicopter Lightning, Phase Two

The Captain's last mention of *helicopter lightning* took place under a hovering Huey and you may recall that it shocked the heck out of four mountain-climbing Nevada concrete workers. After a brief recess to screw up their courage, they gathered bonding wires anew to guide the static electricity to ground. We then resumed the manly task at hand.

Not long after, yours truly transmogrified himself into a Huey logging pilot. Flying over snow-covered logs all day became a love affair with gravity, dancing with Mother Nature every now and then to get our butts kicked.

One gets pretty good with a long-line and remote hook after many years of practice-practice-practice. Good enough to cleverly avoid touching green tree limbs that come between the Captain and the *hooker* far below. *Branches absorb the charge from the hook, and we'll have none of that*, the Captain conspired silently. [The unsuspecting hooker reaches up with a gloved hand, not aware that the remote hook is *hot.*]

Okay, this is actually a *game* that manly heli-loggers play off and on, to amuse themselves. Everybody gets shocked now and then, it is truly inevitable. On a good day, the hook has barely enough *pop* to make one notice. Unless, of course, one is standing in water or one's boots are wet. Then it'll get your attention.

But on a *bad day*—which looks like any other day—the hooker either does a 100-meter dash or ends up on the ground in what is referred to as the *fetal position*. As dark, flat-bottomed clouds gather in the sky, who would notice? The hookers are too busy ropin' logs, and—of course—nobody but a rookie is going to announce over the radio that the hook is *hot*. That takes all the *fun* out of it!

"*Cowboy*" comes to mind, and a heck of a conventional logger he was. He signed on when we were heli-logging up near Libby, Montana. He was good-natured and had a white hard hat with a Stetson shape to it, ergo the nickname. He'd run like a mad man and holler "*Hawww!*" when he was clear. I'd laugh and fly his logs to the landing.

Several days of this mind-numbing activity went by with fair weather. The ground was dry and the Captain was growing bored as the fifth cycle ground along. *One more log-truck load and we'll be off like a prom dress,* I mulled.

Taking "Jeffro's" last turn, I heard a distinct "***pop***" in my helmet's earphones and observed Jeffro doing an animated dance 200-feet below—but making no after-shock-radio-commentary. *Hmmm,* the Captain deduced. The hook is *hot!*

Now why go and spoil Jeff's fun by telling Cowboy that the hook is hot, when Cowboy can find out for himself, both Jeff and I silently conspired. As the Huey's heavy remote hook cleared the last branch between us by inches, Cowboy extended his pink hand and **Lo and Behold**, the legendary *blue spark from hell* leapt from the hook and into Cowboy. Who dropped to the ground and shriveled into the classic fetal position.

To his credit, Cowboy *had* simultaneously crammed a choker eye into the remote hook.

I casually radioed *"Hooker down,"* while safely maneuvering Cowboy's one log "pumpkin" off to the log deck.

"You did that on purpose," Cowboy whined, as I flew away. Jeffro was on his radio fast, laughing his head off for setting up the rookie heli-logger. *"Ha-haaaaaa!"* he chided *Cowboy-in-the-dirt.* "Oh by the way, everyone," Jeff howled, "…the hook is **HOT!**"

That was almost as memorable as the Hignite heli-drill job I worked near Richfield, Utah. This was back when the seismic core-drills were powered by Dodge 360-CID V8 engines and each "move" was composed of four or five "picks." We were flying Lamas then.

As those familiar flat-bottomed cumulus clouds gathered slowly in the sky, I brought the heavy "skid" base unit within reach. Two of the strongest looking guys on the mountain grabbed the half-ton rig like it was a toy and bossed it into position. Working shirtless, they looked like buff gladiators down below, shiny with sweat and determined to set-up the last drill for the day, come hell or…

The compressor came last, the heaviest piece. It took all my Lama had to hover out of ground effect over the skid and hold it stationary while one of the two muscle-bound men reached out to steady the heavy steel unit. He was four feet away when *the blue bolt from hell* suddenly filled the space between his fingers and the nasty compressor.

Gladiator "A" is now doing the advertised 100-meter dash uphill, blowing past the other gladiator, who has seen the messenger— but hasn't gotten the message!

I observed their manly exchange high overhead as gladiator "B" marched blindly into battle and was quickly dispatched in a similar fashion, before he touched the compressor. Off he raced after gladiator A! With no one around to orient the load, I had to set it off to one side of the skid, in order to resume laughing.

Of course everyone knows *"what goes around comes around,"* and the scene for this shocking example occurred just north of Victor, Idaho on a winter seismic job. I had just finished my twenty-day stretch and was going on a ten-day break. Lourdes waited in the truck as I stopped by the magazine to say adios to "Dave," the Powder Guy. Where could he be, I wondered? He's not supposed to wander away from the dynamite.

Lo and Behold, here comes ace pilot Vern Sanders. Flying my Lama, he is hovering high over the magazine, and in need of someone to hook up a load of stump powder to his remote hook. I looked up at Vern. Vern nodded his head and grinned back down at me.

I noticed the terminus of the powder basket's wire choker lying at my feet in the wet snow, and did my pilot buddy a favor by reaching up and slapping it into the *remo…*

I could hear Dave howling with laughter from behind a nearby tree as Vern pulled away with the basket. The static jolt I got from the Lama's rotor blades hit me like a mule kick in the gut, leaving me temporarily paralyzed—curled up like a baby in the snow. Lourdes learned a couple of new English expressions that day, and *fetal position* was among them.

THE MENACE MEETS NENA, THE DENUTTER

Justice in the Idaho Mud

Inhabitants of the little town of Malad City, Idaho live with a mysterious booming noise that comes and goes in the rolling hills south of town. When our Huey logging operation moved into Oneida County, we sought out the property owner of our timber sale to explain the strange phenomenon.

Turns out, there are ancient underground geysers in this geologically active region of the state which vent tremendous jets of steam at unpredictable times. Anyone within a mile or two would be forgiven for mistaking such events as dynamite blasts.

Our customer was a good-natured rancher but said he had stipulations about using his road.

His terms specified that we take care in using the half-mile common easement up the hill to the log landing—a dirt road that the rancher said turned to goo in the event of rain. My mechanic must have forgotten about that the night he got stuck; he wasn't what you'd call a "listener."

An unscheduled shower snuck up on us after I flew in the last load of logs, but the helicopter landing was a mile down the hill so I didn't have to deal with the muddy road. Unknown to us, my mechanic (a meanspirited young fellow known to many as "The Menace") attempted to drive the company's one-ton service van down the road in mention later that evening.

The Menace hit a stretch in the greasy road that tilted left, and not having four-wheel drive, the service van turned into a lead sled and slid off the road—into a ditch. Having no phone in the van to call for help, the Menace got mad and hunkered down for a long, cold night.

When our logging crew met at the bottom of the hill the next sunrise, we noted the white service van not far up the hill, off in the ditch. No one had seen my mechanic, that is, until he came roaring up in his knobby-tired four-wheel drive truck—headed back up the hill toward the van!

Nena Wilkins, the woman who helped supervise the logging lease with the polite rancher was present in our gathering when the Menace went tearing up the rancher's road, flinging mud like all get-out. She was a professional logger who oversaw the log landing and was known to take charge when something went wrong. Something like this here.

Nena had declined driving any rigs up the rancher's road once we left the pavement that morning, it was obvious to most people that the road was unusable. But the Menace had spent a long, uncomfortable night in the service van and was beyond stopping to converse with anyone who had slept in a nice, warm bed. He was going to go get his precious tools and that was *that*.

It is helpful to know that our mechanic was a highly independent sort who didn't have a system worked out whereas it would be noted if he didn't make it "home" of an evening. No wife, no girlfriend, poor rapport with his pilot—no one to miss him. He had gotten stuck less than a mile from an inhabited farmhouse, where most menaces would have walked to ask for help. But no.

Unhappy that no one had come looking for him, the angry Menace thumbed an early morning ride back to the campground to retrieve his four-wheel-drive truck. He then churned back up the hill, determined to secure his tools from the marooned van.

So here he came and there he went up the hill on the rancher's gooey road, countless biscuits of mud flying around like frogs on a hot stovetop. Nena, a woman known to slash off her own hair with a dull kitchen knife, stood in disbelief at what the Menace was doing to the rancher's road.

Closest to the Menace when he drove his truck back down the hill toward us, I could sense Nena, starting to inflate. The self-appointed *Chewer of Asses* for our logging operation was more than ready when the Menace stopped—probably to tell us what a crappy night he had had and whine about not having a 4-wheel-drive service vehicle with a satellite phone.

That's about the time Nena snapped. The poor Menace never had a chance and never got in a word. Her assessment of the situation that muddy morning was not something I can reproduce on paper, otherwise my editor may have a full-grown long-horned cow.

Observers of this exchange might have been reminded of the old "Sergeant Bilko" TV show, where actor Phil Silvers chewed butt frequently and efficiently. Visions of the late Sergeant Ermey in "Full Metal Jacket" also came to mind. That Marine could really sink his teeth in and thrash. But bless his soul, Sergeant Ermey couldn't hold a candle to Nena, *the Denutter*.

On that boggy morning in June, Nena met the Menace head-on. As if trapped in a miniature tornado, she screamed acid-laced obscenities, expectorating and thrashing her extremities— silencing the Menace's lame excuses *and* the nearby booming hills for a moment. The Menace retreated to his camper where he stayed until the rancher's road dried up, and the booming in the hills resumed.

LOGGING THE BIG EDDY

One Mechanic's Hell in Motor Home Paradise

When our heli-logging operation drifted downstream from Avery, Idaho to *The Big Eddy* on the beautiful St. Joe River, our crew had great expectations. Some of these expectations were rational, others were buoyed by reports of a bar with a flat pool table, bubbly-hot pizzas and endless kegs of cold beer. I parked my high-mileage motor home in a cozy spot and set up camp.

The logging started fine and dandy but soon degraded to *anal-oriented mode,* owed to overweight logs tagged end on end to immovable objects—a sure sign that I was either going too fast or the boys were on mushrooms, out of touch with reality on the ground. It happens.

I pickled "Fatty's" overweight excuse for a turn and was about to fly elsewhere for a backup when my roving Huey-pilot's eye caught sight of the fuel quantity gauge—almost at the empty mark! My heart froze in my chest for a second as I crosschecked via the flight-timer.

WTF?! I'm barely halfway through a 1.2-hour logging cycle, according to the timer. I should be entering *maximum production mode*, instead of gawking at the fuel gauge in horror.

I nosed the bird over and radioed the hookers, "*Going for gas, something must be wrong with the gauge. I hope!*" Fortunately for my nerves, the service landing was not far away. Big Al would be waiting with outstretched greasy hands to solve all my problems. Even the ones he caused.

Back safe on the ground, Big Al was standing near the nose when I landed the UH-1H, blowing his red hair straight back as if in a hurricane. Hurrying over, he opened the copilot's door and eyeballed the gauge in mention, having heard about my low-fuel situation on his portable radio.

After shutting the bird down, Big Al took a fuel sample and rose from under the big Bell with a longnecked glass bottle partly filled with Jet-A1—but mostly filled with dirty water!

Tracing the problem back to the fuel tanker, Big Al confessed to having left one of the fuel fill-ports open overnight. It had rained pretty hard, so we suddenly had a contaminated fuel tanker in the all-important logging bird. It was one thing or another in the world of gypo-logging.

Never mind that there was good fishing to be had on the St. Joe, only a short walk from the landing zone. Yes, the bar was right over there, you could hear the billiard balls collide on the pool table whenever a game of 8-ball fired up. I could practically smell the beer. What the heck, *Big Al* was on the job, time to bite a pizza, shoot out the lights, and tilt one for my mechanic.

The next morning, having worked most of the night under the hovering mosquitos, Big Al signed off the bird and I took to the skies. I didn't get very far into the cycle when the roving fuel gauge problem returned, its needle diving and climbing when it should have been steady and reliable.

A weary but determined Big Al greeted me with wiped-out coveralls, shop rags and a smile. In a minute, he was back with more water in his fuel-sample bottle!

It was time to remove the floor panels (we're talking a bucket full of bolts to be removed and reinstalled), open up the fuel cells, and mop out all the water by hand. Fortunately, our employer pulled in behind his two-bladed asset with coveralls on, a sure sign that he came to help. *With* lots of blue shop towels, bless his heart.

It took a few starts and petcock drains to purge the rest of the rainwater from the system but within hours I was back in the blue Idaho sky, searching for some flyable turns among all the aborts. Things fell back into a daily routine after the water scare and Al kept the hatches shut.

It wasn't long before yours truly was on break, headed down the winding road to see my baby. It was two weeks before I checked into the company's new logging operation near St. Regis, Montana. It was there that Big Al briefed me on his last night at the Big Eddy. A gathering of leather clad motorcycle riders moved into the campground, taking over the whole shebang.

Big Al was worried about his helicopter all during the night. He hunkered nervously in his trailer—deer rifle in hand—while the bikers circled around campfires and acted crazy all night long.

Required to rise before dawn, sleepy Al emerged from his trailer, rifle in hand, walking toward a helicopter in the darkness. He hadn't gone very far when he was quickly mobbed by a band of rowdy bikers! Al was dishonorably disarmed and threatened with great bodily harm. Eventually, they let him go. Al went on break after that. (I knew better than to ask him about his deer rifle.)

THE ONE-HANDED MECHANIC

Not by handicap, but by choice

This happened on one of those heli-logging jobs in Paradise, and I kid you not, most of the crew and I were camped out at the Paradise RV Park, right in the middle of Paradise Valley. Montana loggin' in the spring is hard to beat, and it says so, right there on the map!

Of course, "spring" is in March, and there's plenty of nasty weather blowin' out of Canada now and then all the way through May. But mostly it's where you wish you could camp out cheap and work hard year 'round. Or until the unmentionable hits the fan, as it did for one of my favorite one-handed mechanics.

Fred did not appear to have any physical handicaps when we first met. Six feet tall, dark and stout, Fred was a good lookin' young A&P Mechanic. A decade or two younger than this Huey loggin-pilot, but I'd heard from around town that he could truly crew a Huey. I've seen able-bodied men humbled by the task, but it was my job to fly logs and somebody else would have to pass judgement on Fred; unless, of course, he fell short of his responsibilities, somehow.

One of those responsibilities was keeping-up our little corner of a farmer's meadow where the boss had negotiated a sweet deal for our Huey's Service Landing Zone. The entrance to the LZ was near the highway. It was gated, and all around us was nothing but forty acres of fenced, flat pastureland for grazing. Bucolic paradise, at that. Our crafty mobile maintenance unit was already parked level, in the shade of the big tree. And in the midst of the LZ sat the pride of the fleet, the ghostly white *Lorena*.

Lorena earned her keep by flying heavy logs all day long, as fast as we could latch on to them and drop them off at the log landing. At the end of a hard day, flying back to the sunny meadow was always a spiritual event for me, as my bod tingled from hours of bustin' my hump; but I loved it!

I especially loved shutting off all the noise and savoring the sudden silence as I signed my name to records of import. As the Lycoming turbine and composite rotor blades hissed to a stop, I could begin to hear Fred talking under the sputtering of the idling gas truck.

Unstuck finally from the cruel metal seat, I climbed out; more like *poured* out onto the skid's flat toe, then another small step for man, down to the cool green grass with the left Nike and into the fragrant, green cow pie with the right. Sweet.

During all this, my trusty one-handed mechanic has begun his hours-long ordeal of wrenching on, wiping down and refueling *Lorena*. With the main rotor fore-and-aft, our mid-sized service tanker sits ten feet away from the noble UH-1H, the PTO delivering a nice steady flow of Jet-A to the ship's center fuel tank.

A power generator throbs over by the maintenance trailer, powering battery chargers and florescent lights and loud, portable stereo units. *Miss Nibbles*—Fred's ever-present dog—is at my feet sniffing everything and barking loudly at everyone who comes around to *her* LZ. Jack Russells are like that. [Sniff that right shoe all you like, dog.]

I knew it would take Fred longer to do all he had to do, because I seldom recall seeing him without one arm or the other tied up holding on to that precious telephone of his, linked so dependably to an unhappy woman on the West Coast.

Walking his way slowly around the tail section for a general post-flight of the big pieces, Fred was simultaneously talking all "hang-dog" to his far-away wife, with one hand tightly clenched around the cell phone apparently welded to his left ear.

Fred will never hear the last word about *anything*, from what I briefly overheard—much less how to do all his many chores while he's being ranted at. "One more week, honey, I'll be home to fix it then. I'll take the kids campin', I promise. One more week, now remember what we talked about, honey. Aww, come on, now."

Sliding at last into my comfortable ride, my butt feels practically electric and I am ready for the short ride to a Hot Shower in Paradise; but there I go again. [You gotta jump on them metaphors with both Nikes!]

And then came the peculiar large yellow patch in the middle of our previously green LZ. Fred had gone on break by then but there was another sign pointing in his direction: we were short one hundred and fifty gallons of go-juice! The fuel had made it as far as the truck, but careful record keeping showed it had been pumped out.

Yep, you guessed it. Lost in the sound of the generators, barking dogs, and an incessant noise in one ear, Fred had forgotten that he was pumping fuel. Easing up on his professional routine, he allowed himself to be distracted and unwittingly created an ecological disaster that required substantial mitigation. And a new employer for Fred—someplace *far* from Paradise!

THE RAT'S NEST FROM HELL

A Firefighter's Frustration

Romana, CA is the ideal location for a sleepy, country airport. Broad meadows, horse farms, a pond here or there. Sometimes it's so quiet there, my ears sing like power lines in the wind.

It's not always peaceful at the airport. Two noisy retardant tankers and two air-walloping helicopters are based there in the summer, contracted firefighters all. When it's nasty out, there is a comfy helitack lounge, friendly to helicopter and air tanker crews alike—a retreat from the weather, an opportunity to socialize between fire drills. And catch a movie or two.

Ramona can have hectic fire seasons. Other times, it's pretty slow. I spent several busy weeks there before I was able to watch *Silence of the Lambs* from the start. An early mission to the firing range east of town left me dangling: Anthony Hopkins was lecturing a clueless Jody Foster about savoring someone's liver with Italian wine? This really was a *black* comedy, I decided.

Disturbing movies tend to send me off into the sky with irrational fears—pilot-skinning mechanics, for example. *Avoid walking down into dark dungeons at all costs*, I remembered. Shifting back to the Jet Ranger I had ahold of, I wondered about these redundant fires at the shooting range. The last one was started by tracers, so I naturally fretted about what awaited us.

Arriving on scene to a large plume of white smoke, we radioed-in a two-acre spot fire involving dry foliage at the base of a two-story cliff. No shooters in the vicinity. This one could easily be knocked-down with a few buckets of green pond water, my crew of three and I agreed.

Ramona Helitack made quick work of dragging our short-cabled Bambi bucket from the cargo hold, giving me the required operational checks before sending me off to douse the blaze.

"Sal," our helitack base manager, met up with the first water tender to arrive on scene. He began directing a hose-lay from the pond I was dipping out of toward the foot of the fire, as I made several bucket drops and returned to our impromptu helispot, not far away.

In the midst of a three-minute engine cooldown, I noticed a large, heaping rat's nest at my two o'clock, some thirty feet distant. Were my aching eyeballs deceiving me, or was a wisp of white smoke rising from the peak of the nest—a miniature volcano? I smelled some really rank smoke!

Realizing the dry-as-a-bone rat's nest was the perfect model for an energetic fire, I radioed Sal. "A smoldering rat's nest?" He replied. "We're tied up over here, better put a bucket on it."

Music to my ears. Water bucket work is high on my list of groovy things to do strapped inside a hot helicopter. I made brief work of revving up Mr. Lycoming, lifting off smartly so as to minimize my rotor wash on the simmering volcano.

Ooops! After pulling away, a dense cloud of smoke poured out of the nest, telling me I'd better get with the bucket-work or the nest was likely to claim our helispot and keep on spreading.

I had worked long enough with Sal to earn his confidence in my judgement and firefighting abilities. He knew that hauling water buckets around was not the most challenging helicopter work I did. And he respected that. But respect can be fickle, I conjectured, as I flew for my third bucket of water, having missed the heat of the rat's nest with the first two.

It's true! I missed a relatively easy target a total of three times, blowing my rotor-headed mind in the process. The only excuse I have is that there was zero wind. A max-gross, out-of-ground-effect bucket drop using a short lanyard called for smooth tail-rotor pedal-work.

Aerodynamically speaking, there was a short *moment* involved between the cargo hook and the bucket, turning a relatively simple task into a swinging *hit-or-miss* affair.

After my third unsuccessful drop, Sal and the crew hoofed-it back to the helispot to appraise the flaming rat's nest firsthand. The igloo-shaped mound of tiny interwoven sticks was fully involved by then, putting out lots of heat. There was plenty of mud surrounding it, thanks to me.

Strike three and you're out?

Good thing we had a pumper crew backing us up and plenty of hose. I watched them address the problematic nest with nozzles while I swatted persistent deer flies with a battered ballcap.

The crew didn't spare me their acidic taunts on the chatter frequency after my third drop, trust me. I sulked among dead flies, waiting for *vermin-en-fuego* to be put out, the old-fashioned way.

THIRTY BELOW, AND FEELING IT!

Who's covering my six?

I should have known that my first flying assignment to Wenatchee, Washington's Icicle Creek would come in the dead of winter. "Fine," I said. "The Huey loves cold air." It didn't matter about me.

Cold air is just what you need when you're long-lining big, fat (burnt) logs off steep terrain running the length of the canyon. Density altitude? Forget about it! Not a factor. Fill the bag with go-juice and load up the log trucks. That's how we rolled at Icicle Creek. And logging was good.

The hookers were celebrating the fact that most of their logs were flying without the usual fussing over weights. It seemed like anything they hooked up would fly, there were tons of torque available in this atmosphere and engine temps were in the green.

Visitors were stopping at the log landing, watching from a safe distance as my sister ship and I brought in turn after turn, pumpkin after pumpkin. The landing rat radioed that a former Vietnam Huey pilot had watched for an hour, saying he'd never seen a Huey do such awesome work. My helmet grew tighter.

So many helicopter-harvested logs plugged the log landing that the loader operator was taxed to stack them into decks, creating towering monuments of wood on either side of the road. Log trucks struggled to keep up, the mills were sawing a glut of cellulose and everyone seemed happy. And then it happened.

213

Racing out of Canada, Arctic air blew into Wenatchee Valley and froze everything in sight. Oh, the helicopters survived okay, we had our precious Hueys wrapped up in weather tarps overnight. Getting our gasoline generator to start at thirty degrees below zero (Fahrenheit) was another thing. Until the generator starts, the space heater won't ignite and a work crew's shivering (and swearing) begins in earnest.

Fortunately for me, my better half was aware of me freezing my butt off every winter. Lourdes had zeroed-in on a winter clothing sale at a massive sporting goods outlet in a distant metropolis. The Big Box was packed with shoppers when we got there, but to our amazement, there were two fine-looking snowmobile suits available in my size. "Buy one, get one *FREE*," the sign said. So we did.

Ergo, I feared not the Arctic blast when it came and was pleased as punch to fly logs from the rays of dawn until the arrival of dusk. Or at least until something broke, which happens all too frequently in the heli-logging business. Only this time, it would be the danged loader, and it didn't exactly break. It simply wouldn't start. Diesel #2 stops flowing at thirty below, wouldn't you know?

Snug as a bug in my new outfit, I drove over to the log landing along with my frozen mechanic to observe firsthand what was transpiring with the frosty loader—maybe we could help and get back to work sooner? Driving through a stark valley of logs, we spotted the yellow loader with its grapple frozen to the ground.

The loader operator was directing his glowing space heater's heat signature into the open engine compartment in an effort to thaw the slushy diesel fuel enough to start the massive machine's miserable motor. The stench of diesel and heater exhaust permeated the air. An hour went by and nothing moved.

One can only sit so long in a crew-cab pickup listening to *Top 40* radio and/or a disenchanted workmate, so I soon joined those gathered around a lively fire many meters from the yellow steel. The cold was intense once we transitioned outside, so the fire the chasers built really hit the spot. We got close to it.

As the warmth soaked into our bones, tongues loosened up and soon we were telling tall tales and swapping lies as if there was no truth to be found anywhere around Wenatchee. We felt free to bury our boots in all the bullshit. Finally warm, I decided to go visit the loader operator, still thawing away.

"Whoa, Wingo, your ass is on fire!" I heard someone shout from behind me. Spinning my head around, my wide-open eyes were rewarded with the sorry sight of melting rip-stop nylon, dripping off what was left of the backside of my new snowmobile outfit—from my rosy cheeks down to my bulky boots!

Suddenly I was reminded that it was thirty degrees *below zero*. My tidy-whities were doing very little to keep my backside from turning into twin cakes of ice. A chorus of manly jeers and whistles arose as I retreated to the toasty crew-cab, trailing smoke. The seat bottom was too cold for my bare butt! I had but one thought in mind: getting back to my camper and climbing into that *free* snowsuit of mine.

TOLD YOU SO!

But he shouldn't have

Driving onto the remote, crunchy-white helicopter LZ early that snowy Sunday morning, I oriented the F-100 service van's headlights directly at the Huey and put 'er in park—unaware that I was helping erase the tracks of an overnight thief.

By the time my trusty mechanic and I had the tarps rolled up and the space heater warming up the interior, the sun was just beginning to light up our jolly November morning.

And then I opened the UH-1's left bubble door and it hit me: I had left my expensive white flight helmet hanging on a hook high above the Bell's left seat Friday night—something I don't normally do. It was <u>not</u> hanging where it should be!

Our gyppo logging outfit took the Sabbath off, so come Sunday morning, here we were to go to work. Except for one thing. There was no $800, custom-made, super-lightweight, size-seven helicopter flight helmet hanging where it should be. I was vexed!

"Jack" (the pilot of the other UH-1 on our logging sale) drove up to see what the radio chatter was all about. When I explained that someone had apparently stolen my flight helmet, his demeanor was impassive—saying only, "told you so."

Jack was trying to twist things around, actually. When I originally came on the job, he was in the habit of parking his Huey in a little trailer park in the next valley. Convenient for him, his fancy new work trailer was parked there.

There were a couple of problems with this arrangement, I perceived: 1) the company would have to eat the extra flight time to fly two helicopters to the logging sale and back every day. And 2) seasonal valley fog trapped the helicopter(s) at the trailer park in the morning until the sun heated things up and the fog slowly lifted—hours later.

Having seniority on our logging operation, I parked N84NW off a logging spur on the timber sale and asked Jack to do the same with his bird. He chose to wait until the next morning to reposition his bird, but the predictable fog had him trapped. Meanwhile, I was up on the mountain, making money—keeping my crew employed while freezing their butts off.

Getting back to the morning of the theft, I turned my back on Jack after his "told you so" comment. I gathered my mechanic and hookers around to conduct a daylight search around the LZ. It was hard to give up on my trusty helmet; so many memories involved.

I finally told my conscientious mechanic of my decision to "call it," then radioed the Woods Boss to advise him of the problem. About then my wrench motioned to me that he had a David Clark headset with him. Like any well-prepared professional A&P mechanic, he had come to work prepared to fly, and he was willing to share his headset with me.

I had *never* logged without a helmet before, but our hungry woods crew needed to work, so the borrowed headset saved us from missing any production. Even the log truck drivers were happy by day's end.

Having flown with that headset while logging in a single engine helicopter—one of the most dangerous jobs in the USA—I must say I can't recommend it. I spent too much time worrying about my fragile head, distracting me from the hazardous goings-on below me.

Jack went on to finish this job and both crews migrated to the next sale, high above a tributary of the Salmon. By then Jack had taken a shine to a little beauty who worked on the log landing—a curvaceous, smoky-eyed chaser-lady who just so happened to be married. The two started flirting over the logging radio and it took off from there.

Their ill-advised liaison led to late Saturday night dancing at a distant Idaho bar while the beauty's betrothed was cutting timber near St. Regis. There was a buzz going on among our logging crew, and it wasn't good.

Then it happened. The lady's cuckold husband got wind of the debauchery and took to drinking. He unfortunately also took to driving, ultimately losing control of his truck, leading to the death of another motorist on a curve in the dead of night.

After that, Jack and the little lady vanished—but life went on for the rest of us.

Years later, the owner of our gyppo operation climbed out of his F-250 one afternoon and with a stern look, handed me a business letter he had just opened. It was a neatly typed application from none other than <u>Jack</u>, inquiring about logging pilot openings? The boss asked me to handle it, at my leisure.

There's a thing they say about karma: what goes around, comes around?

In my short response to Jack, I mentioned that the timber faller (the one Jack royally screwed over) was back to work killing trees for us—after serving jailtime. So, we were still getting over his last work shift, *thank you just the same.* I was too much of a gentleman to add, "I told you so."

WHERE DID SCOTTY GO?

Secrets Under the High Plateau

When our Huey-loggin' outfit moved to the high plateau overlooking Lake Payette north of McCall, Idaho, we were very happy to be working the summer in "*God's Country.*" Except for the fact we'd be logging at the ragged edge of a Huey's performance, *aka* high-density-altitude.

I considered myself fortunate to have a mechanic who was well known to me, someone I trusted like a brother. "Scotty" and I had worked more than one job together, crewing fire-fighting Lamas in the High Sierra—or pushing tin in and out of the main hangar back at home base. Scotty was "*The Man!*"

On remote logging jobs like this, it was not uncommon to find the field mechanic camped out in his trailer adjacent to the helicopter "service landing." From there, it was a hop, skip and a jump to work every morning for a Huey mechanic who went to bed late most every night.

Scotty was too cheap to spend good money on a trailer. He had a substantial emu ranch under way back in Oregon, the place he called home. In the field, he spent precious little on himself. Most of his *per diem* money was being reinvested in emu egg-incubators and fencing materials.

So, instead of living in town in a thirty-dollar-a-night pink motel room or camping out in a trailer next to the bird, Scotty did all his eating and sleeping in the company's one-ton Ford service van.

Never mind that the van was already fairly full of tools, parts, manuals, and lubricants. Scotty saved space by cooking on a Coleman stove and eating everything out of the same skillet, needing only a large spoon and a fork to round out his silver service. AM radio for the news.

He made his bed on a three-quarter-inch plywood board in the van. No mattress, or even a pad.

I for one admired my mechanic's determination in saving his hard-earned money. He was one tough character, as far as I was concerned. I pampered him whenever I could, but he took a lot of pride in not asking for favors, or complaining about conditions whenever it hailed hard, or nights were lonely and cold.

I had been working on my logging memoirs during this time with Scotty, which probably made me more introspective about him than your average, *devil-may-care* logging pilot. I put myself in his shoes frequently: when I was cozy in my motorhome, enjoying a good movie from the DVD player, Scotty was wrenching away on a tall ladder, or huddled in his stinking sleeping bag.

Driving up the logging road to "service" every morning before dawn, the tops of three large boulders would come into view, then a tall dead snag, then our faithful Huey. I could depend on Scotty having done the morning inspection and signed-off the maintenance logbook by then.

There were no little blue buildings anywhere on this state-sponsored fire sale, so pilots took their "breaks" in a nearby weed patch, and I assumed that our mechanics did the same. They had work shovels, after all—but many weeks would go by before I needed to borrow Scotty's shovel.

It turns out that the suits who worked for State Forestry back then paid little heed to the Service Landing. Their forest had burned down a year before our materialization, after all, so they were primarily concerned with harvesting the salvageable timber and planting new trees. Why would they question where our mechanics "went"—as this writer did—months into the project?

So it finally came to pass that we were in a mid-day maintenance break, and I inquired of Scotty where "the head" was. Scotty pointed toward the three prominent granite boulders, adding, "the blue shop towels are in the van." *Darn it*, I had some *Charmin* back in the motorhome.

The boulders were over twenty-feet high and arranged in such a manner that, as you walked through the two closest to service, a shady grotto would come into view. And from one end to the other of this stinky retreat, there were HUNDREDS of *used* blue shop towels strewn about, and months of unburied *business*.

In shock, I suddenly no longer needed a shovel. I was not going to contribute to the *bad news behind the boulders*. I had gleaned something important, though. I knew where Scotty *went*. And it's not an easy thing to get out of one's head.

FLYING INTO HOT WATER

Once upon a time, I received a call from a California operator who regularly sent his UH-1s south of the border to help during the Mexican fire season. "We'll fly there together, get you started on a fire contract and relieve you in a couple of weeks," the chief pilot promised. "The regular pilot sprung his back and needs to rest up." Sounded like a plan that my domestic partner might okay.

Before loading up the Cadillac, I made a list of things to pack, starting with bug dope and ending with reading material. T-shirts, flight suits, shorts, socks and boots: check. I emptied every seam and pocket of my travel pack to make sure that there was nothing to cause me any grief. I was confident my attention to detail would green-light me through Customs inspections without so much as a raised eyebrow.

The chief pilot (let's call him Harley) was a former military man my age, highly experienced. Harley ruled over a seasoned squad of spray pilots and medium-lift firefighters. He asked me to come in two days before departure, and handed me a heaping box of aeronautical charts.

"You're going to navigate and help fly us all the way to Tuxtla, a few hours south of Mexico City," he instructed. "Us" included Harley, myself, and an A&P mechanic, headed south for the fire season.

Our Bell 212 was being buttoned up in the outfit's hangar following a 100-hour inspection. Once I had our 2,000-mile ferry flight meticulously planned, Harley had me go over the ship with a fine-toothed comb and get familiar with the cockpit layout.

Takeoff was planned for dawn the next morning, giving me another night in a pink motel, and a "breakfast" that left me wondering where the *breakfast* was, in my breakfast.

When I drove up to the helicopter early that April morning, I couldn't help but notice the ship was bulked-out with luggage, incidentals and spare parts—stuff needed for a 300-hour inspection.

Fueling up on a slick cement pad, the mechanic used a come-along to keep the skids from over-spreading as the ferry tank was topped-off. We managed to get all our stuff on board and removed the skid restraint.

It was going to be a hot one. Harley tucked his flight jacket behind the left seat and started buckling up as the sun broke the horizon. He was brave enough to have me do the max-gross takeoff, right down the sleepy airport's asphalt taxiway.

Our route took us through Blythe, California to Casa Grande, Arizona and points south, refueling every two hours or so. After a rudimentary inspection in Hermosillo, Mexico, we flew southeasterly, getting to know each other.

By the time we did our first overnighter in Los Mochis, I was more familiar with the Chief. He was a Harley rider when he wasn't flying and he was married, with dogs. He also had me flying a 212 with an *out-of-rig* tail rotor and *zero* force-trim control.

This made for a long ferry flight, chasing the *ball-in-race* back and forth, trying to find a sweet spot in the pedals that simply wasn't there. The Chief explained that the rigging would be checked again further down the road, and we pressed on.

My mechanic pal and I would be budget-limited to regular rooms at our first motel, I learned. The Chief boasted that his per diem afforded him the best accommodations at every stop.

I wasn't complaining, looking around my quarters for the night. I'd seen the inside of a Mexican prison, so my room—by comparison—was a VIP suite.

Rising early, we climbed hard to cross the Sierra Madres. Refueling at Durango, we headed southeast for *Aguas Caliente*, last stop before we overnighted again in beautiful Leon. At the Aquas Caliente airport, Harley and the mechanic took breaks while I supervised refueling with *turbosina*.

And right about the time I began to enjoy this little adventure, here came an armed *Federale* in green camo fatigues, leading an alert-looking German Shepherd, straight for our helicopter. I like canines, but I knew better than to interfere with a working variety, so I relaxed and let the two do their thing.

Turns out the dope-sniffing dog was VERY INTERESTED in our helicopter! He began whining loudly and straining at his leash, clawing his way toward the left front seat, leading his excited handler toward our personal effects.

The dog was doing his best to jump into the ship and go after our bags. I got eye contact with the handler and assured him, "We have NO DRUGS, NADA!" The Federale appeared not to hear me, giving the dog enough slack to reach Harley's gear. By then, Fido was going bananas. The Fed admitted he'd never seen his dog so worked up!

About the time I figured my gringo friends and I were going to be spending the night in jail, Harley reappeared. When he saw the hubbub with the service dog, he let out a big laugh. The Federale allowed Harley to reach in and grab his jacket, precisely what the dog was going ape over.

"My Shepherd's in heat. She needed a hug when I left home yesterday, ergo her scent on my jacket."

Ho-ho-ho, what a relief! I enjoyed the moment, knowing the local prisons are highly overrated.

MY BABY WAS AN ELEVEN

A Eulogy to my Lover

Dating Lourdes was always a fun time for me. She was goodhearted. Her smile never failed to perk me up, make me forget my worries. We could be perfectly happy socializing in her family home in Tierra Blanca, Mexico. Fumbling through our Spanish/English dictionaries, we would patiently look for the right words to fit the moment: *Gorgeous.* Charming. *Irresistible.* Intriguing. *Captivating.* Intoxicating. All this fun amid thirteen children in their family.

I found new meaning in the old Al Martino standard "*Spanish Eyes.*" Lourdes owned the kind of peepers the composer dreamed of when he penned the song perfectly suited for her. Another that matched her to a "T" was Sammy Kershaw's "*She Don't Know She's Beautiful*" ... "*she never was that kind.*" This, too, defined *Lourdes Maria Medina de Alarcon.* Or "Lulú" for short.

We courted to the music and lyrics of Barry White, a black singer we both appreciated for his sensational love ballads. Riding around in the backseat of Juan Rangel's Ford *Thunderbird*, I found Miss Lourdes worthy of Mr. White's phrasing and praises of the woman he adored.

Lourdes had a great sense of humor. We found oodles of things to giggle about around each other; a kind of culture-clash magic that let everyone know we were a *pair*. Lourdes' innocence, her charm, her natural radiance, and her hour-glass-figure—there was a lot to like!

But hold it right there. Lourdes was bashful about being seen in a dress. I understood *why* the first time I saw her so. The woman had strong, muscular thighs, but below her knees were two *palitos,* skinny little sticks with mere hints of gastrocnemius muscles—neither the *laterals* nor the *medials*. She was insecure about exposing her "toothpicks." She lacked *Olive Oyl's* courage.

Spending Sundays together at the beach, or sitting in my helicopter explaining how the switches and dials worked, we got to know each other better. Lourdes worked as the senior secretary for a judge in the local *jusgado.* I went with her to her employers more than once, sitting patiently in the court's visitor seat while Lourdes got caught up on her typing. And how that girl could type!

Lourdes had what I would call an advanced capability when it came to typing. Working on manual IBM typewriters, her normal speed was right around one hundred words-per-minute. I personally typed maybe forty words per minute on my best day back then, so I was in awe of her typing skills, especially her error-free technique.

The court required one original and four copies of each document, so Lourdes had to work with four sheets of carbon paper to produce the required number of copies, and the documents had to be error-free and smudge free or the judges wouldn't sign them. Lourdes presided over four other secretaries, all in the same office—typing away like noisy robots. They seldom looked up.

It would be eighteen months from the time we met until we were able to overcome the hurdles to her legal immigration into the U.S.A. We were reunited in Albany, Oregon in November of 1977 and were later married in sunny Reno, Nevada, during a break from my job as a helicopter pilot.

We often joked about my gas problems or her skinny legs. I'd suggest she had to wear a dress on the 11th of every month, stuff like that. At 11:11 o'clock, morning or evening, Lulu should be standing in front of a full-length mirror. When the elastic in her socks aged a little, there were no calf muscles for them to hang onto, so they would fall into little turtlenecks around her ankles.

I pointed out to her once how I remembered which street to turn on to reach her sister's house in the high desert town of Hesperia. *Easy*, turn left on *11th street*—remembering Lulu's *palitos*. She would usually poke me amid such revelations, yet laugh along with me at the same time.

But we both knew the truth. If Lourdes had had perfect legs, I would never have had the opportunity to meet her. She would have been swept up by a young Mexican attorney, for sure!

Of the 21,993 days Lourdes was to live upon this green earth, she devoted 13,496 to me, as my faithful wife. Lulú helped me raise three great kids. They grew to love their mom as much as I. There were so many wonderful times together. And there were days that we feared the next dawn. But we lived thirty-seven years sharing the kind of love I think few couples experience.

Was it within her power to leave us on the 11th day of October, 2014, following a long struggle with Hodgkin's lymphoma, my poor baby? Or was it Lourdes' way of saying,

"Don't cry for me.
I am free of the body which no longer worked.
Rejoice, Lulú has wings!"

THE DEVIL IS IN THE DETAILS

High Risk Poker, Played Badly

While attending the September 30th gathering of the Professional Helicopter Pilots Association at the Riverside Airport in 2017, I was approached by a handsome dark-complected male in civil attire who had been listening to the lecture delivered by my great friend, Pete Gillies.

The gentleman introduced himself as an airborne law enforcement officer from the greater Los Angeles area, and that he was interested in my *book*. [Pete had pointed me out to the audience.]

He looks like a cop, I thought, shaking the man's hand.

"*Yes, feels like a pilot's hand*," I said aloud, adding, "I have *three* books. Which one would you like?"

"I want your *Captain Methane*," he said with a smile.

"All three of my books have '*Captain Methane*' in the title," I informed the cop: he was not the first to remind me of my *ignorance* through r*edundancy*. "I have one of each in my travel bag."

"Oh, that's *okay*," he said, happily. "I can order it *online*, right?" He wanted no autograph, then.

"You are certainly free to do so, yes," I hated to add, anticipating the one-dollar commission many months from this day versus an eight-dollar profit from selling the one I brought with me.

"*I wanted to ask you,*" he leaned close to me, titling his head slightly. He suddenly seemed more interested in talking, now that he didn't have to shell out any bucks for a lousy book. "*How do you go about writing your stories?*"

"That's *easy*," I replied, looking him dead in the eye. "As soon as I type in the title, the story begins writing itself." Taking a breath, I finished him off with: "as if ink spilled down the sheet of paper, the words forming from inky little puddles."

The law enforcement officer from greater Los Angeles stared back at me as if I had cheated him out of a great literary revelation. I stepped backward one step, ready to make an about-face in his honor, when the devil grabbed me by one shoulder with a terrible grip, sinking his claws in deep.

"Ohh, ho ho, *Captain Methane*, you are not allowed to divulge how it is the stories came to be. Remember our *little deal*?" The devil hissed......"***Sssuck-ahhhh!!***"

[Blinding flash of light, followed by stinky cloud of sulfur and a bag full of ashes.]

ACKNOWLEDGMENTS

It's a dangerous thing to start naming the people in your life who came to your aid mentally, spiritually, financially, or simply as a brother helping a brother. But it would be wrong not to credit the good souls who have helped edit 100-plus stories over the years. Some boosted my morale between disasters, so I really must thank:

David Busse, it was an honor and a pleasure flying with you and the Riverside, California ABC Eyewitness News crew. We flew many miles and covered several important assignments together—having fun at most of them. *Except* at the Salton Sea during the epic fish die-off.

Frank Ertl has been most generous with his time and camera equipment over the years, sharing good books, joining me in lively conversations about everything from guns to helicopters. This guy can *really* cook, I must add!

My BFF Pete Gillies, who taught me everything about flying helicopters that the Army couldn't. I was so, so fortunate to be able to work with you and your angelic wife, Pat for many years.

Dennis Finn is a schoolmate from the old Las Cruces HS Red Band, a very talented drummer, computer scientist and friend for fifty-five years. We have so much in common, old pal. Thank you so much for helping float my boat during some troublesome low tides.

Ryan Forsythe, what groovy karma that you are living along the West Fork of the Illinois River in the very cabin my friends and I built back in the mid-1970s. The additions you and Kaci have made make me grateful for sparing the towering trees critical to your habitat. Better yet, you both are experienced teachers and publishers, essential elements for making *Bush Pilot!* come to life.

Michael Hardy, Wes Brown and Gary Buck are three of my Smokejumper buddies and one-time neighbors in Oregon. Big strong men who selfishly lend their time and talents to help a friend.

My favorite heli-logging "hooker," Jeff Holder inspired me to document our most outlandish and noteworthy characters. Logging for Skyline in Montana accounted for many such groovy tales.

Ilse Irwin, my brilliant German teacher, who laughed at my crude cartoons (of her) and twisted my arm to take an art class, learn to cartoon? (I was high on motorcycles at the time—sorry Ilse.)

My *other* BFF Steve Mankle, who was the subject of many of my cartoons and close to my heart for more reasons than I can go into. I wrote many a good story from the massive desk Steve drove 200 miles and installed for me. A Smokejumper from the *Gobi*—you "the Man!"

My Vietnam mentor Mike Mullenix, aka *"The Elephant Brander"* in my autobiography, flying with you over the bad guys was an honor. A born leader. You and Troy are amazing together.

My longtime New Mexico friend Steve Owen, who has lent his keen eye and sound advice for so many years—through four books, now. Grateful to have known you, I learned *mucho* from you.

Vertical Magazine's Editors Elan Head and Oliver Johnson must be credited for helping foster a plethora of memories that became illustrated tales in their fine publication. When I felt I had run out of nonfiction tales, Oliver somehow turned my story-spigot on again. How *did* you *do* that?! Elan, you have inspired me to dig deep and keep at it. You are such a talented woman and pilot!

Matt Thurber, how fortunate to have you as a friend and confidant all these years. You have been so unselfish with your time and top-level skills. It's hard to imagine you as a helicopter "swamper" back in the day. What character building work that was, eh, Matt?

My big brother Jon Lance Wingo, who taught me some of the finer things in life, made me proud to be his brother—and flew me up, down and upside down in an A-1 Skyraider. Thanks to "The Colonel" for the sharp eye for details and critiquing movies or novels. *I'm so* lucky to be your little brother!

Thanks to the following promoters for their courtesies, including media credentials and sharing my trackside photos from Costa Mesa, Industry, Inyokern, Orcutt, Prairie City, San Bernardino, Ventura and Victorville. I was trackside with my Canon at hundreds of exciting races in California. Steve Evans, Kelly Inman, Dave Joiner, RC Jones, John LaDouceur, Brad Oxley, Steve Stasiefski and Howie Zechner? Speedway promoters at the top of the heap.

ACKNOWLEDGMENTS

Randy Mains, you're a concerned air ambulance pilot's homing beacon—and a writer's writer. I'll long be grateful for your unselfish support and advice. You must be credited with waking up the commercial air ambulance industry to invest in higher performance helicopters, true IFR capability, and two alert, IFR-rated pilots up front. That's the way to do it. And it's not cheap.

My favorite research engine is Google. I can open up the world with Google at my fingertips. Life for this writer would be a real drag without access to this powerful tool.

ABOUT THE AUTHOR

DORCEY WINGO lived his youth in the southwestern United States, the son of school teachers. He grew up dreaming of becoming a pilot, finally earning a pilot's seat after being drafted into the US Army. Returning to civilian life, Wingo eventually found work in what became the "Golden Age of Helicopters." He was married to a wonderful lady from Culiacan, Sinaloa, for 37 years, fathering three children. A story teller at heart, Dorcey amassed a total of 15,000 flight hours and published over 130 stories. One publisher has compared Dorcey to Mark Twain. A widower now, "Captain Methane" continues to write and lives alone in southwestern Oregon, surrounded by a large herd of cats.

ABOUT THE ILLUSTRATOR

Since **CHRIS ROHRMOSER** could hold a pencil in hand he has never stopped drawing airplanes and helicopters. Ask his parents, who were forever supplying him with paper. Later in life, the pencils became paintbrushes and the doodles became full-blown colour illustrations. Chris still can't believe his good fortune in having been part of the aviation community for so long, not as a pilot but as an illustrator who has used his imagination to share his artwork with those who are. Chris lives in Victoria, British Columbia, Canada—walking distance from a floatplane terminal and busy helipad.